The BBC presents the 108th season of Henry Wood Promenade Concerts

BBC PROMS

ROYAL ALBERT HALL, LONDON • 19 JULY – 14 SEPTEMBER 2002

Welcome to the BBC Proms 2002, a celebration of great music, available to all.

This year it's fiesta time, as we explore how the rhythms and melodies of Spain have stirred the imaginations of composers around the world. We hear the echoes of Spain in works by Chabrier, Lalo, Bizet, Ravel, Rimsky-Korsakov, Richard Strauss and others, and we trace the true Spanish tradition from the roots of flamenco, through the passionate polyphony of Victoria, to the entrancing short operas of Falla and Granados.

William Walton, whose centenary we celebrate, went back to the Old Testament for the text of his rousing choral classic *Belshazzar's Feast*; other ancient biblical tales inspired major works by Handel, Haydn, Mendelssohn, Britten and Stravinsky.

A weekend with Valery Gergiev and the Kirov brings Musorgsky's *Boris Godunov* and Gubaidulina's acclaimed new *St John Passion*. We welcome back the Royal Concertgebouw Orchestra with Riccardo Chailly and the LA Philharmonic with Esa-Pekka Salonen; James Levine makes a belated Proms debut with his Munich band; Simon Rattle conducts his first Mahler 8; Mariss Jansons, Bernard Haitink, Pierre Boulez and Christoph Eschenbach all return.

A wide range of BBC commissions includes new madrigals for the King's singers and a set of new variations for the Last Night; the BBC Symphony Orchestra premieres major new works by Anthony Payne, David Sawer and Mark-Anthony Turnage, and the music of international composers Marc-André Dalbavie, Roberto Sierra and Osvaldo Golijov is heard at the Proms for the first time.

The Proms continue to introduce new audiences to classical music. The *Blue Peter* Prom picks up the fiesta spirit, while Oliver Knussen's magical Sendak operas will inspire new artworks in collaboration with London schools. The Children's Prom in the Park is back, as is the 'Nation's Favourite' Prom. Wynton Marsalis returns, Renée Fleming and Bryn Terfel share an afternoon of song, and *Oklahoma!* marks the Richard Rodgers centenary.

Last year the Proms responded to the events of 11 September and proved once again that music could have a uniting, healing force; this year tradition returns refreshed for the Last Night. Every Prom is available as always on BBC Radio 3 and now online, and there will be more televised Proms than ever before on BBC1, BBC2 and the new free digital channel BBC4. The BBC Proms are at the heart of everything the BBC does to make music accessible to everyone. They are your concerts: enjoy them.

Nicholas Kenyon

Nicholas Kenyon
Director, BBC Proms

Contents

C000121480

Your Guide

How to Book

1895　1927　1941　1947

The Proms were founded to bring the best of classical music to a wide audience in an informal setting. From the outset, part of the audience has always stood in the 'promenade'. Prom places originally cost just a shilling; today, standing places at the Royal Albert Hall still cost only £4.00, and over 1,000 tickets go on sale for every concert from an hour before. Programmes have always mixed the great classics with what Henry Wood, the first conductor of the Proms, called his 'novelties' – rare works and premieres. **1895** The 26-year-old Henry Wood launches the Promenade Concerts at the newly opened Queen's Hall in Langham Place, close to where BBC Broadcasting House now stands. Wood goes on to conduct the Proms throughout their first 50 years. **1905** Wood composes his celebrated *Fantasia on British Sea-Songs* for a special Trafalgar Day concert. **1927** The BBC takes over the running of the Proms. **1930** The newly founded BBC SO becomes the orchestra of the Proms; the BBC's own orchestras still provide the backbone of the season. **1941** The Proms move to the Royal Albert Hall after the Queen's Hall is gutted in a German air raid. **1942** The BBC SO shares the season for the first time with another orchestra, the LPO. **1944** Henry Wood dies shortly after celebrating his Proms jubilee. **1947** The Last Night is shown on TV for the first time. **1950** Malcolm Sargent becomes Chief Conductor of the BBC SO. **1953** The first out-of-London orchestra appears at the Proms: the Hallé, from Manchester, under John Barbirolli. **1955** First Proms visit by the National Youth Orchestra. **1960** First BBC Proms commission: William Alwyn's *Derby Day*.

1996   1998   2001   2002

1961 First complete opera heard at the Proms: Mozart's *Don Giovanni*, courtesy of Glyndebourne Festival. **1966** First foreign orchestra to play at the Proms: the Moscow Radio Orchestra, under Gennady Rozhdestvensky. **1968** The First Night moves from Saturday to Friday in order to accommodate a memorial concert to Malcolm Sargent, who had died the previous year. **1970** The first Late Night Prom features cult pop group The Soft Machine. **1971** First world music to be heard at the Proms: a sitar recital by Imrat Khan. **1974** First Pre-Prom Talks. First brass-band concert at the Proms, given by the combined Black Dyke Mills and Grimethorpe Colliery bands. **1994** The Proms celebrate their 100th season with a survey of past premieres. **1995** The Proms celebrate their centenary year with a season of brand-new commissions. **1996** Launch of Proms in the Park, Proms Chamber Music and the Proms Lecture. **1997** Evgeny Kissin gives the first Proms solo recital. **1998** First Blue Peter Family Prom. **2000** First series of Poetry Proms at the Serpentine Gallery. **2001** Leonard Slatkin becomes Chief Conductor of the BBC SO. **2002** The Proms go digital with a fortnight of broadcasts on the new BBC FOUR.

Picture credits:
Peter Joslin Collection (Queen's Hall;
Henry Wood in the ruins of
the Queen's Hall, 1941)
BBC (Proms programme)
Chris Christodoulou (Royal Albert Hall
podium and Blue Peter Prom)
Giovanni De Bei (Proms in the Park)
Carlo Faulds (Leonard Slatkin)
Alex von Koettlitz (Royal Albert Hall ceiling)

The BBC: 75 years of bringing the Proms to you – on radio, television and now the internet too
www.bbc.co.uk/proms

viva españa!

Spanish with a native accent

To the click of castanets, the strumming of guitars and the stamp of dancing feet, Calum MacDonald charts the unstoppable spread of Spanish music from Andalusia to Latin America and beyond …

The folk music of Spain is among the richest and most immediately identifiable in the world. Perhaps in no other country (or countries, once Spanish culture had spread to Central and South America) have the principal composers drawn so thoroughly upon it. Yet paradoxically the 'Spanish National Style' we recognise instantly in such works as Falla's *Nights in the Gardens of Spain* or Rodrigo's *Concierto de Aranjuez* was crystallised in the works of foreign composers (Russians and Frenchmen, mostly) who imitated Spanish characteristics to write works of exotic regional colour, encouraging Spanish composers in turn to create an authentic national concert music of their own.

Centuries of invasions and immigrations – the Visigoths, the Moors, the gypsies – brought successive musical ingredients into Spain. The cross-cultural mix fermented potently in the southern region of Andalusia, the home of flamenco: and, in the minds of non-Spaniards, it is often the flamenco style that stands for Spanish music as a whole. Yet 'Spain' as a single country has always been a fragile concept. It arose from several once-independent

kingdoms, each with its strong regional cultural traditions, and some (such as Catalonia and the Basque country) with their own languages. It was also forged in the fire of the war to drive out the Moors – who for centuries, at the height of *their* culture, had controlled large tracts of the Iberian peninsula and left an indelible oriental colouring on this western land, as palpable in the regional musics as in the ornately intricate architecture of the Alhambra.

The Moorish influence engendered dances such as the *jota* of Aragon and

Navarre, accompanied by castanets, and the Andalusian *cante jondo* (literally 'deep song'), ornate and passionate in character with soulful or highly rhythmic guitar accompaniment, and dances such as the *sevillana* and *seguidillas*. The music of other regions was simpler, or more austere as in Castile and Léon. In Catalonia the *sardana*, a round-dance performed in the street, became an important expression of national identity. The slow *fandango* of the Basque region was imitated by Gluck and Mozart; the hypnotic rhythm of the *bolero* would be taken up by composers from Chopin to Ravel.

Despite such musical vigour at the popular level, art music was slow to emerge in Spain itself. The regional Spanish kings, more concerned to drive out the Moors, did little to patronise the arts until after the country was unified under Ferdinand and Isabella; but, during the late Renaissance, church music especially experienced a tremendous flowering, with the emergence of masters such as Morales, Guerrero and, above all, Victoria. Though national characteristics can be traced in their work, essentially they

LEFT
A Maja and Gallants, 1777, by Francisco Goya

RIGHT
The 'Court of the Lions' in the Alhambra Palace, Granada, the former citadel of the Moorish kings of Spain

TOP RIGHT
A 19th-century Spanish painted paper fan showing scenes from a bullfight

Tomás Luis de Victoria (c1548–1611)

Missa pro victoria
Prom 68

Born in Avila and a contemporary of St Teresa, Victoria worked in Rome before becoming chaplain and choirmaster to Philip II's sister in Madrid. Generally considered Spain's greatest composer of the Renaissance, he was a master of ornate polyphony and wrote mainly religious choral works. Unusually for the time, Victoria was able to have almost his entire output published during his lifetime in the forms he intended. The *Missa pro victoria*, one of his most famous works, is a 'battle mass' based on the French chanson 'La guerre' by Janequin.

belonged to the great European hegemony of Catholic polyphonic church music. There were few major instrumental composers, despite a vigorous tradition of keyboard composition and of music for the *vihuela*, the lute-like forerunner of the guitar. The guitar itself arrived during the 17th century and, immediately

important as an accompanying instrument for song, was soon furnished with a vast repertoire of popular dance pieces by such virtuosi as Gaspar Sanz. The characteristic tuning of the guitar, with its strumming *rasgueado* chords, deeply infuses Spanish music of all kinds.

Under the Bourbons, foreign composers found congenial employment and inspiration in Spain: notably Domenico Scarlatti, whose keyboard sonatas echo the sounds of the guitar. But homegrown Spanish sonatas were written by Antonio Soler, and Spain in turn exported great musicians like the brothers Pla from Catalonia, internationally celebrated oboe virtuosi and composers of trio sonatas mixing a high *galant* style with earthy evocations of folk dancing. Spain produced no symphonic master in the classical era (though the precocious genius Arriaga, who died at 20, showed signs of becoming one). But the guitar now found its greatest virtuosi in composers like Fernando Sor, who vastly enlarged its scope as a concert instrument with bravura studies, variations and dance pieces. The tradition of guitar music was continued throughout the 19th and 20th centuries by such figures as Tárrega, Barrios and the Brazilian Villa-Lobos.

Yet until the mid-19th century vocal music predominated, especially for the stage. The *zarzuela*, the indigenous variety of light opera with spoken dialogue and musical set-pieces in strongly national style, was one of the most vigorous (but essentially

Pablo de Sarasate (1844–1908)

Zigeunerweisen
Prom 39

Born in Pamplona, Sarasate was a wunderkind who gave his first violin recital at the age of 8 and went on to win a phenomenal reputation as a performer worldwide. Lalo, Wieniawski and others dedicated concertos to him. As a composer, Sarasate mainly wrote bravura fantasies to show off the virtuosity of his instrument, but often made use of 'gypsy' style to do this, as in his ever-popular *Zigeunerweisen*. His four books of *Spanish Dances* were also influential in disseminating the national idiom among violinists.

unexportable) expressions of Spanish culture; in parallel, the folk music on which *zarzuela* drew had become an ever headier brew. Gypsies arrived in Spain during the 16th century; by the 19th century they were as ubiquitous popular entertainers as the Hungarian and Romanian gypsies of the Austro-Hungarian empire. In Andalusia especially they created a new and livelier form of the *cante jondo*, the *flamenco* (literally 'flamingo') style of song and dance, full of improvisation, free ornamentation and fierce emotion. South and Central America, with their mix of Spanish immigrant, native and Creole populations, had meanwhile developed their own dances, such as the *habanera* and *tango*, which were then imported back into Spain.

With the Romantic era, which encouraged a cult of local colour in art in parallel with the growth of nationalism and a renewed sense of regional identity,

ABOVE
Isaac Albéniz: his friend Turina recalled him in later life 'sitting at the piano – not to play, which he was hardly able to do any more – but to perform a strange version of his *Iberia* in which his hands, his voice and even his Cuban cigar – which, in complicated spirals of smoke, resembled the garland of notes that decked the pretty melodies of his "Triana" – all played a part'

BELOW
Enrique Granados (caricature)

composers began to move towards a much more conscious use of idioms and dances derived from regional folk music, rather than the almost automatic symbiosis that had existed before. Yet Spanish composers were slow to follow this road. Internationally, the best-known examples of 'Spanish' music were being created by outsiders attracted by the strong character of what they knew of that exotic country – Russians like Glinka (in his *Jota aragonesa*) and Rimsky-Korsakov (*Capriccio espagnol*) or Frenchmen like Chabrier (*España*) and, above all, Bizet, who never visited Spain in his life yet whose *Carmen* fixed the character of the Spanish gypsies and the seductive Andalusian style in the European consciousness more powerfully than any other single work.

The Spanish violinist Sarasate – who produced a popular *Carmen Fantasy* on themes from Bizet's opera, and was the dedicatee of Lalo's *Symphonie espagnole* – was among the first composers to consciously exploit his country's musical riches. He was followed by Albéniz and Granados, piano virtuosi and persistent opera composers. The 'missing link' in this story is the Catalan folksong-collector and editor of Spanish Renaissance music, Felipe Pedrell, whose own operas earned him the sobriquet of 'the Spanish Wagner'. His attempts to reform Spanish music were

Enrique Granados (1867–1916)

Goyescas
Prom 18

Granados's opera is, uniquely, based on a pre-existing cycle of piano pieces, also called *Goyescas*, in which he sought to evoke the sombre, passionate and colourful Spain depicted in the paintings of Goya. The decision to turn these brilliant pieces into an opera was a further development in bringing a 'Goya-esque' world to life. Thus the libretto, set on the streets of Madrid and dealing with the tragic rivalry of a bullfighter and a soldier over the beautiful Rosario, was written after most of the music was composed. The 1916 New York premiere was a stunning success, but Granados was drowned on his homeward journey when his ship was torpedoed by a German U-boat in the English Channel.

equally based on making available the richness of the peninsula's diverse folk-music traditions and the glories of its early polyphony, so that Spanish composers could know their own resources and effect a new synthesis. A tireless teacher and proselytiser, he inculcated the highest artistic ideals and gave real direction to the careers of Albéniz, Granados and Manuel de Falla, who all studied with him or sought his advice.

The vital achievement of Albéniz and Granados was principally in piano music: the former's

… composers began to move towards a much more conscious use of idioms and dances derived from regional folk music …

Manuel de Falla (1876–1946)

The Three-cornered Hat
Prom 7

El Amor brujo
Prom 24

The only woman to arouse the interest of the famously austere Falla, a lifelong bachelor, is said to have been the gypsy dancer Pastora Imperio, around whom he composed the first great Spanish national ballet, *El Amor brujo* ('Love, the Magician'). This tale of magic, in which a girl is haunted by the ghost of her ex-lover, gave him plenty of opportunities for brilliant and fiery dances in flamenco style. *The Three-cornered Hat*, written for Diaghilev's Ballets Russes and premiered in London with décor by Picasso, is a more sharply humorous work of social comedy, drawing on a wider repertoire of folklore and full of telling guitar effects in the orchestration.

Iberia and the latter's *Goyescas* (germ for the later opera of the same name) are perhaps their age's defining expressions of Spain through the medium of the keyboard. The prolific Turina followed their lead in exploiting Spanish colour and regional features with a new refinement and contrapuntal expertise. But it was Falla above all who performed the vital synthesis that took Spanish music decisively into the 20th century. Though instinctively a man of the theatre, after early attempts at *zarzuela* Falla realised he needed a vantage-point outside Spain. He found it in Paris, where he went for a seven-week stay and remained for seven years. Decisive meetings with Dukas and Debussy confirmed him in his path. In Falla's view Debussy, the composer of *Soirée dans Grenade* and an orchestral *Ibéria*, had become 'spellbound by an

imaginary Andalusia'. Falla now saw his own way forward as the creation of an 'imaginary folklore' for Spain by the transmutation and combination of folkloric elements in highly sophisticated scores.

Debussyan impressionist techniques, used with a piercing Iberian clarity, suddenly allowed the 'national' elements, derived from folk and popular song and

BOTTOM LEFT
The Three-cornered Hat: set design by Pablo Picasso for the ballet's premiere production at the Alhambra Theatre, London, in July 1919

BELOW
Manuel de Falla: a 1920s portrait by Ignacio Zuloaga

Manuel de Falla (1876–1946)

La vida breve
Prom 26

Master Peter's Puppet Show
Prom 51

Falla had penned half-a-dozen unsuccessful *zarzuelas* before he wrote his first important stage work, *La vida breve*, as an entry for a competition. It won, but the promised performance did not materialise. In Paris, Dukas took one look at it and recommended it for performance at the Opéra-Comique. A simple love-tragedy, it was the first example of Falla's unique synthesis of Spanish *zarzuela* and *flamenco* traditions with the latest French advances in harmony and orchestration. *Master Peter's Puppet Show* is a later and much more multi-faceted creation. Written for private performance, it mixes puppet and stage action in its retelling of an episode from *Don Quixote*, superbly imagined for chamber orchestra in a basic neo-Classical style combining references to Spanish music of many different periods and regional styles.

dance (and, in his later music, from the Renaissance polyphony), to speak with a new vividness and intensity. But here nationalism is no longer provincial nostalgia. Falla was as much a European modernist as Bartók or Stravinsky. But his advances could not be easily sustained: he wrote very little in the last 20 years of his life, concentrating on the vast oratorio *Atlántida*, which he did not live to complete. Albéniz and Granados were already long dead, and Turina, whatever his talents, was no modernist.

In the other arts, a new and vigorous modernism – represented by the painters Picasso, Miró and Dali, and by the poet-dramatist Federico García Lorca

INSET RIGHT
Miles Davis and the original LP cover design for his 1960 jazz album *Sketches of Spain*

BELOW
Roberto Gerhard

Roberto Gerhard (1896–1970)

Concerto for Orchestra
Prom 7

Though of mixed Swiss-German and Alsatian parentage, Gerhard was Catalan by birth and affiliation. He studied first with Granados and Pedrell, then with Schoenberg in Vienna and Berlin, but it was only after he was forced to leave Spain at the end of the Civil War, and settled in Cambridge, that he really began to develop his individual approach to Schoenberg's serial methods. Towards the end of his life Gerhard was writing some of the most challenging and sonically-inventive music anywhere, though still with very 'Iberian' contrasts of light and dark, as exemplified by the explosive *Concerto for Orchestra* of 1964.

– flourished between the wars under the new Spanish Republic. Falla collaborated with Lorca, but the potential leader of the next generation, combining an intimate knowledge of folk music with what he had learnt from Schoenberg in Berlin, was Pedrell's last pupil, the Catalan Roberto Gerhard. The Spanish Civil War, which destroyed the Republic and drove Falla, Gerhard and other progressive composers into exile, artificially retarded any such development. General Franco's ultra-conservative regime imposed a strong central power and suppressed all attempts at regional autonomy, which he feared would lead to separatism, especially in those regions that had supported the Republic. This led to artistic censorship and a downgrading of independent cultural expression, including a ban on the Basque and Catalan languages.

By default, a continuation of the 'Andalusian' style was allowed to predominate, and perhaps to outlast its natural span, though at this late stage it found one of its principal masters in the blind, prolific and immensely popular Rodrigo, whose numerous concertos have become one of the principal tonal representations of Spain to the wider world. Rodrigo's international reputation has tended to overshadow other gifted composers such as Mompou and Montsalvatge, who put their own individual spin on the approved national idiom.

But a much more radical outlook flourished in the cultural diaspora of Spanish America, especially Mexico,

Joaquín Rodrigo (1901–99)

Concierto de Aranjuez – Adagio,
arr. Miles Davis and Gil Evans
Prom 24

The blind composer from Sagunto was an impeccable international ambassador for Spanish music. Among his many works, he composed (in Paris, like a good Spaniard) the world's best-loved guitar concerto, the *Concierto de Aranjuez*. Its plangent slow movement – an evocation of the *saeta* ('arrow of grief', an ancient form of sacred flamenco sung during the annual Easter procession through Seville) – has been transcribed many times for different media. Miles Davis's much-extended swung version for jazz trumpet and ensemble, occasionally surreal in its effect, paradoxically reinforces the music's deep emotion.

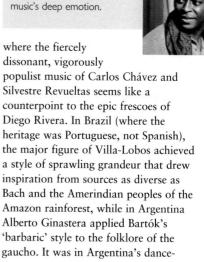

where the fiercely dissonant, vigorously populist music of Carlos Chávez and Silvestre Revueltas seems like a counterpoint to the epic frescoes of Diego Rivera. In Brazil (where the heritage was Portuguese, not Spanish), the major figure of Villa-Lobos achieved a style of sprawling grandeur that drew inspiration from sources as diverse as Bach and the Amerindian peoples of the Amazon rainforest, while in Argentina Alberto Ginastera applied Bartók's 'barbaric' style to the folklore of the gaucho. It was in Argentina's dance-bands that the tango transcended itself into a new art at the hands of the popular master Astor Piazzolla.

The contemporary Argentine Osvaldo Golijov has followed Piazzolla's lead in attempting a new synthesis of popular and classical elements, drawing on tango, his ancestral Jewish roots and sophisticated modern techniques both in small-scale works like *Last Round*

Silvestre Revueltas (1899–1940)

La noche de los mayas
Prom 26

Sensemaya
Prom 41

Homenaje a Federico García Lorca
Prom 58

The most original figure in Mexican music, Revueltas was born around midnight on 31 December 1899. Forty years later he died of pneumonia, brought on by overwork and alcoholism. A true original, his short life was packed, like his scores, with incident, colour and disturbance. (Aptly, *revuelta* means a 'revolution', a 'fight', a 'turning-point'.) A convinced Communist, he worked for the Republican government in the Spanish Civil War and wrote a musical homage to the poet Lorca (assassinated by the Nationalists). The turbulent showpiece *La noche de los mayas* was originally a film score evoking the glory and barbarism of the ancient Central American civilisations.

and in large-scale pieces like his recent *Pasión según San Marco*, composed to the same millennium commission that prompted Sofia Gubaidulina's *St John Passion* (see page 71).

As the post-war dictatorship loosened its grip, various Spanish composers looked again towards the 12-tone serial style to bring a new expressivity into their music. Chief among these were Cristóbal Halffter and Luis de Pablo, though it can hardly be said that they have established an international profile rivalling Rodrigo, who was raised to the nobility by King Juan Carlos before his death in 1999. Spain is again a monarchy, but also a functioning democracy, and the cultural expression of its regions is once again tolerated and even encouraged. The signs are that Spanish music has survived into the 21st century with its rich and various heritage still a living force.

BELOW
The Castillo of Kukulcán at Chichén Itzá, the ancient Mayan city in central Yucatán

The new online directory of music awards, including organ and choral scholarships, and music awards at independent schools and choir schools.

www.music-is-it.com/awards

register online NOW

at **www.music-is-it.com/proms** (even if you're not interested in the new awards directory) & you could win a fabulous DVD player and vouchers in our free prize draw!

MUSIC-IS-IT DOT COM: THE SMART MUSIC PORTAL | WEBSITE DESIGN | ONLINE MUSIC SMARTCLASSIFIEDS DIRECTORIES: JOBS PERFORMERS COURSES TEACHERS RETAILERS

OXFORD
UNIVERSITY PRESS

music now

2002	gerald barry	50
	john buller	75
2003	anthony powers	50
	zhou long	50

...and then

2002 william walton 100

oxford university press
repertoire promotion department
70 baker street
london w1u 7dn
tel: +44 (0)20 7616 5900
fax: +44 (0)20 7616 5901
repertoire.promotion@oup.co.uk
www.oup.co.uk/music/repprom

CONDUCTING
YOUR INVESTMENT
WITH STYLE

Call us on **020 7506 6500** or email us at
marketing@rlam.co.uk

Royal London Asset Management
is regulated by the FSA.

www.rlam.co.uk
MEMBER OF THE ROYAL LONDON GROUP

Royal London
Asset Management

Edinburgh International Festival 11-31 August 2002

choice

Only in Edinburgh can you see **Claudio Abbado** conduct *Parsifal* directed by Peter Stein, **Scottish Opera** continue its Ring Cycle with *Siegfried*, **Luc Bondy's** production of Britten's *The Turn of the Screw*, the **Vienna Burgtheater** perform Schiller's *Mary Stuart* or **the Ro Theatre** perform *Macbeth*. And then there's the **Orpheus Chamber Orchestra**, the **Gustav Mahler Jugendorchester, Los Angeles Philharmonic Orchestra, Ian Bostridge, Christian Tetzlaff, Richard Goode**...

just a select few of the events in the 2002 Edinburgh International Festival. And we have added one more reason to come – **The Royal Bank £5 Nights**. Twenty five late evening concerts offer a huge range of music, performed by some of the world's leading artists. From Bach to Stockhausen, from song recitals to chamber music, from orchestral music to Indian Raga, at just £5 for every seat you can afford to experiment. Your only problem will be what to choose!

For a brochure with full details call 0131 473 2000. **www.eif.co.uk**

Edinburgh
International FESTIVAL

Opera | North

✓ No annual fee

✓ **2.9% p.a.** for Balance Transfers, fixed for six months from the date your account is opened

✓ **15.9% APR** (variable)

✓ Up to 59 days interest free on retail purchases when you pay your balance in full and on time each month

With Exclusive Benefits, this is the Credit Card to suit your lifestyle*

- Discounts on tickets paid for in full with your Classical Arts Visa Card for a wide range of concerts throughout the year, including LSO and Opera North Events, and many more
- Complimentary Souvenir Programmes for certain events
- Discounts on selected live CD releases
- Two free tickets per year for a selection of concerts
- Discounts on hospitality packages
- Discounted subscription to Gramophone
- Exclusive Cardholder Prize Draws and offers

*Full details of all benefits will be sent to you with your card.

TO APPLY CALL FREE ON

✆ **0800 028 2440**

Please quote IEE4

When calling, please have to hand your bank details and account information of any loans or credit cards that you currently have.

Spanish with a foreign accent

James Harding explains why so much of the most famous 'Spanish' music seems to have been written in Paris or St Petersburg

TOP RIGHT
Pola Negri *(centre)* as Carmen in Ernst Lubitsch's 1918 silent movie, known in America as *Gypsy Blood*: 'Until you see Negri,' declared *Picture Play*, 'you have never seen a real, honest-to-badness Carmen'

BELOW
'Like a mad bull in the arena': Emmanuel Chabrier at the piano (sketch by Florian)

Most people have a Shangri-La, a land real or imaginary, a Paradise where they can indulge their day-dreams and escape the greyness of everyday life. In English, we talk about 'building castles in the air'. In France, the phrase is 'faire des châteaux en Espagne' and composers have long been among the keenest of castle-builders.

Emmanuel Chabrier (1841–94)

España
Prom 1

First performed in 1883, *España* would, boasted Chabrier, 'arouse the whole audience to a fever pitch of excitement'. It did, and quickly established itself in the repertory, although modesty crept in later when Chabrier described it as 'a piece in F, nothing more'. Largely self-taught, and thus often dismissed by the Establishment, he was to prove a much keener innovator than many conventionally trained composers. Like much of his other music, *España* contains novelties ahead of its time. As for his Hispanicism, Falla always insisted that no one did a better *jota* than Chabrier.

Bizet did not really belong to this select group. Spain and its music were for him simply a means of creating atmosphere and background in *Carmen*. Emmanuel Chabrier, on the other hand, was not only a leading member of this happy band, but the most flamboyant. He loved Spain, food, women, art and music, though not necessarily in that order. Plump, vivacious, 'like a mad bull let loose in the arena', as one observer remarked, he was apt to massacre pianos with his volcanic playing. For such a larger-than-life character the colour and warmth of Spain were irresistible.

Chabrier spent a whole season in Andalusia, where he listened greedily to the *malagueñas* and *zapateados* he heard in between admiring the pretty women he saw on the beach. They had 'fine breasts', he reported, 'and often neglect to fasten up their costumes: from now on I'll be carrying buttons and thread with me. I'm always keen to be of service.' In Seville he marvelled at the Andalusian behinds 'wiggling about like frolicsome snakes'. In Granada he was lost in wonderment at the *señoritas*'

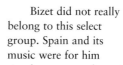

Georges Bizet (1838–75)

Carmen – extracts and arrangements
Proms 3, 39 and 65

When the composer of *Carmen* was asked why he had never visited Spain, he replied: 'It would cramp my style.' Bizet's aim was to achieve a representation of Spain that would satisfy the preconceptions of French audiences. The novel that inspired *Carmen* was, after all, by a Frenchman, and the libretto was the work of two more. It was enough for Bizet to imbibe colour from Spanish songs which he studied in Paris and to leave the rest to his imagination. Indeed, *Carmen*'s famous 'Habanera' uses the melody of an art-song that Bizet mistook for a Spanish folk tune. The paradox is that, following its initial failure, *Carmen* soon became the 'Spanish' opera *par excellence*.

tiny hands and exquisite arms, adding, 'I won't let on what the women display, but they display it beautifully.'

So he came home and wrote *España*, a very French and very personal impression of Spain. Three decades later

the famous trombone solo was to be echoed in Stravinsky's *Petrushka*. Yet *España* was never very popular in Spain. Although another Hispanicist, the Russian Rimsky-Korsakov, spent a much shorter time in the country than Chabrier – a period of three days off Cadiz during his service as a naval cadet – it did not prevent him from composing an equally exuberant *Capriccio espagnol*.

Édouard Lalo was an ardent Hispanicist too, but he went one better than either Chabrier or Rimsky in that

Édouard Lalo (1823–92)

Symphonie espagnole
Prom 1

Lalo's *Symphonie espagnole*, premiered (like Bizet's *Carmen*) in 1875, pioneered the Hispanic mood in French music. Although written in concerto style, its five movements display Lalo's preference for the symphonic development and solid orchestration he had learnt from German models, especially Schubert and Mendelssohn. The work calls for a large orchestra and is based on extracts from popular Spanish songs which it knits adroitly into a multicoloured whole. The provenance of the Spanish material is vague, but it serves as an exotic component convincingly dressed up in terms of 19th-century French Romanticism and as a springboard for some virtuoso display.

he could actually claim Spanish ancestry, being descended from a family that had emigrated from Spain to Flanders in the 16th century. There was, indeed, something of the cast-iron Castilian in his distinguished features. He worked on his *Symphonie espagnole* with the young Spanish virtuoso Pablo de Sarasate, to whom he also dedicated his Violin Concerto. The combination of Lalo's experience as an accomplished violinist and viola-player with Sarasate's unique flair resulted in a *Symphonie espagnole* that adroitly absorbs fragments of traditional Spanish folksong into the techniques of French symphonic music. (Among Sarasate's own compositions designed to show off the silvery sheen and ice-cold sweetness of his masterly playing were his *Zigeunerweisen* – 'Gypsy Airs' – and *Carmen Fantasy*.)

If Lalo could boast a remote Spanish ancestry, the credentials Ravel was able to offer were even more impressive. Ravel's mother, who played so important a part in his existence, was a native of Aranjuez. He was born in Ciboure, a little coastal town near the Franco-Spanish border, and took great pride in his Basque origin. Manuel de Falla observed that 'the Spain of Ravel was a Spain inherited as an ideal from his mother, whose exquisite conversation, always in fluent Spanish, used to delight me when she reminded me of her youth, which she had spent in Madrid ... I understood then what fascination these ever-present memories

ABOVE
Édouard Lalo: a Hispanophile French composer of distant Spanish descent

LEFT
Arrangement in Black: Portrait of Señor Pablo de Sarasate, 1884, by James Abbott McNeill Whistler

had exercised on her son during his childhood – enhanced, no doubt, by the power that any reminiscence derives when a song or dance theme is inseparably linked to it. That explains the attraction Ravel felt from his earliest days for a country of which he had often dreamed. And, consequently, when he wished to characterise Spain musically, he favoured the rhythms of the *habanera*, the most fashionable of the songs that his mother had heard … This is why the *habanera*, the supreme element of all Spain, has continued to live in French music, although Spain herself forgot it half a century ago …'

In his early twenties Ravel had already composed the *Habanera* for two pianos which he later orchestrated as the third section of the *Rapsodie espagnole*. This opulent work is his most spectacular homage to the country he loved best next to France. Falla, a strict judge in such matters, praised his free use of the Spanish rhythms and ornaments which he had deftly assimilated into his own individual style. Spaniards did not care much, however, for *Boléro*, which remains none the less Ravel's most popular work, and one which, thanks to a recent extension of copyright, earns a reputed million pounds a year in royalties. It was, perhaps, Ravel's cavalier treatment of the traditional Spanish dance form that upset them, for instead of the usual bright and vivacious style of the conventional *bolero*, he produced a hypnotic and long-drawn-out study in

Nikolay Rimsky-Korsakov (1844–1908)

Capriccio espagnol
Prom 27

Rimsky-Korsakov's mastery of brilliant orchestration enthralled the young Debussy and Ravel. In his *Capriccio espagnol* of 1887, Rimsky aspired above all to 'dazzling orchestral colour'. This he contrived by draping rhythms such as the *fandango* and the *alborada* in sumptuous instrumental trappings. While purists may not approve of his glittering showmanship, it continues to seduce audiences with its irrepressible gusto and powerful attack. Rimsky saw the Spanish themes he exploited as a rich source that would lend itself to all sorts of cunning effects. He thus carried on a tradition inaugurated by Glinka, the first composer to signal a Russian interest in Spanish music. Rimsky's Hispanicism may not have been very authentic, but it is as exhilarating as champagne.

RIGHT
Ravel in his pyjamas (1909): portrait by Achille Ouvré

INSET RIGHT
Nikolay Rimsky-Korsakov: portrait by Valentin Serov

crescendo (Ravel himself insisted it was 'all orchestral tissue and no music').

Ravel's other 'Spanish' works include the *Pavane pour une infante défunte*, which qualifies on the grounds of its pretty title alone, and *Don Quichotte à Dulcinée* (his last completed work), a set of three songs that grew out of an abortive project to write music for a film starring Fyodor Chaliapin (the music was finally written by Ibert instead). To these may be added the *Vocalise-étude en forme de Habanera*, an exercise in the rhythm that haunted him all his life; the *Alborada del gracioso*, which exists, like so many of Ravel's works, in versions for piano and

Maurice Ravel (1875–1937)

L'Heure espagnole
Prom 18

L'Heure espagnole, premiered at the Opéra-Comique in Paris in 1911, was billed as a *comédie musicale*, although it is not so much a 'musical comedy' in the English sense as an *opéra-bouffe*. The play it was founded on is a typically French farce by the Parisian wit Franc-Nohain, yet Ravel discovered in it what he called 'the opportunities for making use of the rhythms of Spanish music'. Thus one high point of the score is an arietta that blossoms into a *malagueña*, while the final ensemble for all five characters (the clockmaker, his wife and her three lovers) is a delectable *habanera*.

orchestra; and the one-act *opéra-bouffe* *L'Heure espagnole*, its punning title referring both to its running-time (approximately an hour) and to the grandfather clocks that serve as hiding-places for the lovers of a clockmaker's wife in 18th-century Toledo. And if *Tzigane* is not strictly of Spanish inspiration, it at least has the macho arrogance of consummate showmanship.

How do the unlikely names of Richard Strauss and William Walton fit in with all this? Because the *Don Quixote* and *Don Juan* of the one and *Christopher Columbus* of the other at least imply a dalliance with Spanish culture. Neither of them was as committed as Debussy, even though his acquaintance with the country went no further than a quick day-trip over the border to San Sebastian: after briefly witnessing a bullfight, he returned to France. Despite this, Debussy's grasp of Spanish idiom was intuitive, as he showed in the piano piece *La Puerta del Vino*, inspired by nothing more than a picture postcard of the Alhambra. With another piano piece, *Soirée dans Grenade*, he achieved a powerful evocation of the Spanish character without at all relying on the traditional dance forms and melodies that Lalo had called into service. It was 'nothing less than miraculous', declared Falla.

Debussy's masterpiece in the Hispanic idiom is, without a doubt, the orchestral suite *Ibéria*. Here he reproduced in music, often with novel and subtle results, all that Spain meant

ABOVE
George Raft and Carole Lombard in Paramount's 1934 film *Bolero*

LEFT
Set design by Maurice Sendak for the 1987 Glyndebourne Festival production of Ravel's *L'Heure espagnole*

TOP RIGHT
Claude Debussy (1884): pastel portrait by Marcel Baschet

Ronald Grant Archive (above); © Maurice Sendak (left); Lebrecht Music Collection (top right)

Debussy's acquaintance with Spain went no further than a quick day-trip over the border … After briefly witnessing a bullfight, he returned to France

Claude Debussy (1862–1918)

Ibéria
Prom 54

Debussy's *Ibéria*, the second of his three orchestral *Images*, is the most concentrated and ambitious of all his 'Spanish' works. First heard in 1910, its three movements open with a depiction, or 'image' (the composer was acutely sensitive to pictorial art), of the stark sunshine and black shadows of streets and byways, continues with the perfumed mystery of the night, and ends with an exciting festival celebration. The score is filled with effects that evoke the essence of Spanish music with deep understanding. Debussy 'made it clear', said Falla, 'that he did not intend to write Spanish music, but rather to translate into music the associations that Spain had aroused in him. This he triumphantly achieved.'

to him and all the associations it drew forth from his creative genius. His use of guitar effects, as Falla acknowledged, even stimulated Spanish composers to emulate him. With *Ibéria* the Hispanicism of French composers reaches its height. It is not just 'Spanish' music: it is music written by a composer who blended revolutionary techniques with an intimate perception of the Spanish heart.

'Spanish and Latin-American' music at the Proms

Anderson	Alhambra Fantasy	Prom 58
Bernstein	The Magnificent Seven	Prom 65
Bizet	Carmen – extracts/arrangements	Proms 3, 39 and 65
Chabrier	España	Prom 1
	Habanera	PCM 2
Copland	El salón México;	
	Latin-American Sketches	Prom 41
Crumb	Songs, Drones and Refrains of Death	Prom 58
Debussy	Ibéria	Prom 54
Gershwin	Cuban Overture	Prom 41
Henze	Fandango	Prom 8
Holt	Canciones	Prom 51
Lalo	Symphonie espagnole	Prom 1
Mozart	Arias from Don Giovanni	
	and The Marriage of Figaro	Prom 29
Ravel	Alborada del gracioso	PCM 2
	Boléro	Prom 3
	Don Quichotte à Dulcinée	Prom 29
	L'Heure espagnole	Prom 18
	Pavane pour une infante défunte	Prom 45
	Rapsodie espagnole	Prom 16
	Tzigane	Prom 39
Rimsky-Korsakov	Capriccio espagnol	Prom 27
Rossini	The Barber of Seville –	
	overture; 'Largo al factotum'	Prom 29
Strauss	Don Juan	Prom 25
	Don Quixote	Prom 36
Walton	Christopher Columbus – suite	Prom 11
Wolf	Spanish Songbook – selection	PCM 5

CRÉATEUR D'AUTOMOBILES

RENAULT

The new Vel Satis. Luxury motoring redefined by Renault, sponsoring BBC Proms in the Park event, Hyde Park. For more details telephone 0800 072 33 73 or visit www.renault.co.uk

Rhapsody in Metallic Blue.

VEL SATIS

THE ROYAL OPERA
COVENT GARDEN

SOME OF THE FINEST CONDUCTORS IN THE WORLD
AT THE ROYAL OPERA HOUSE 2002/3

New Season opens September

Colin Davis • Christoph von Dohnányi • Edward Downes • Mark Elder • John Eliot Gardiner

Philippe Jordan • Charles Mackerras • Antonio Pappano • Simon Rattle • Mark Wigglesworth

For further season details and to book online visit – **www.royaloperahouse.org**
Box Office **020 7304 4000** (Mon–Sat 10am–8pm)

"When It Came Down To Quality
THE CHOICE WAS EASY"

Windows should not only look sensational. They should also keep you safe from intruders and be maintenance free in all weathers.

That's why more than 600,000 people have asked our advice before installing new windows and doors into their home. They trust a company awarded a record eight BSI kitemarks, a 10-year guarantee that's been outlasted more than three times over and skilled installation teams trained and employed only by BAC.

Our web site offers an (immediate online quotation) free and has a virtual house where you can see which style of window would suit you best.
Simply log on to **www.bacwindows.co.uk** now.

Or if you prefer, you can call us for free for more information. **Call today quoting reference Proms.**

You might be very glad you did.

freephone
0800 666 444

www.bacwindows.co.uk

Living with the best

BOOTHROYD STUART
MERIDIAN©

Meridian Audio Limited
Stonehill, Stukeley Meadows
Huntingdon, England PE29 6EX
Tel (0)1480 445678 Fax (0)1480 445686

http://www.meridian-audio.com

Living with the best quality sound and video can be a compromise.

At Meridian Audio we have the solution. We make what is now recognised as the world's finest audio and video system for the home.

Meridian digital surround sound systems have been designed from the start to provide the best music *and* a great home theatre.

All our products from CD/DVD players to the latest in digital loudspeakers work as a matched system controlled from one handset so you can have the best of both worlds – performance without compromise.

Bringing down the house

Stephen Johnson explains how tales of biblical heroes like
Samson have inspired composers from Handel to Stravinsky

'Originally, above all in the period of the Kingdom, Israel stood in a correct, that is to say natural, relationship to all things. Their Yahweh was the expression of their consciousness of power, of their delight in themselves, their hopes in themselves: in him they anticipated victory and salvation. This state of things long remained the ideal, even after it had been tragically done away with: anarchy within, the Assyrian from without. But the people retained as its supreme desideratum that vision of a king who is a good soldier and an upright judge.'

Friedrich Nietzsche, *The Anti-Christ*

It is fascinating to find such enthusiasm for the Bible in the man who called Christianity 'the one great curse, the one great intrinsic depravity'. But for Nietzsche there was a quality in the Old Testament – the sacred writings of the Jewish people – that was woefully lacking in the New. For Nietzsche, the ancient Kingdom of Israel was a land fit for heroes – for beings who reflected his own ideal of 'The Superman'.

Read some of the best-known stories of the Old Testament afresh and

Nietzsche's somewhat slanted praise becomes easier to understand. There we find Jacob, who wrestled with God, and forced him to grant his blessing. He is also rewarded with a promise: 'Because you have been strong against God, you shall prevail against men.' We find the valiant, passionate King David, slayer of the giant Goliath and lover of women and music. We also find muscular prophet-heroes, like Elijah, who challenges the heathen god Baal to a kind of divine trial of strength, at the end of which Baal is effectively annihilated.

So we should not be surprised that so many composers have been drawn to these invigorating, if occasionally baffling, tales. George Frideric Handel may be best known for his New Testament-based *Messiah*, but the vast majority of his oratorios take the Old Testament as their starting-point. Take *Samson* (begun immediately after *Messiah* and premiered in London in 1743). Loosely based on Milton's *Samson Agonistes*, it tells of a warrior of supernatural strength, defeated by the wiles of a woman and enslaved to the Philistines, but finally victorious as he brings down the Philistine temple on

his own and his enemies' heads. For the writer Julian Herbage, Samson was 'the first, and greatest, of Handel's heroic oratorio tenors'. Even as he tells of the misery of defeat and slavery, Handel's Samson retains a profound human dignity. For Herbage, this was epitomised by Handel's use of the obviously masculine tenor voice, in contrast to the male alto protagonists of his operas: 'His Hebrew leaders thus attain a virility unknown to the more effeminately cultured emperors and princes of the operatic stage.' Herbage was writing in the early 1950s; since then ideas about the relative value of Handel's operas and oratorios have shifted – along with notions of 'virility' and 'effeminacy'. But Samson remains an outstanding tragic hero, magnificent but flawed, superbly contrasted with the voluptuous, manipulative Dalila. (This season also offers Prom-goers the chance to compare Handel's Dalila with her more fully-fleshed 19th-century Romantic incarnation in Saint-Saëns's Samson opera of 1877.)

The story of the prophet Elijah seems to have had a similar galvanising effect on the imagination of Felix Mendelssohn. However fine some of the music for his oratorio *St Paul* may be, as drama it is eclipsed by *Elijah* (premiered in Birmingham in 1846). The contest between Elijah's God – the true God of Israel – and Baal has a pace and vividness unlike anything else

LEFT
Samson and Delilah
by Peter Paul Rubens

29

in Mendelssohn. As the people's prayers to Baal grow ever more desperate, Elijah taunts them majestically: 'Call him louder, for he is a god! He talketh; or he is pursuing; or he is in a journey; or, peradventure, he sleepeth ...' But Elijah too is fallible. With his life now threatened, he flees into the wilderness, only to be struck down by depression. Elijah's aria 'It is enough! O Lord, now take away my life' may not quite plumb Handelian depths, but it had enough dignity and pathos to make it an institution in this country until well into the last century.

Something of the grandeur and theatricality of *Elijah* may have left its mark on William Walton's smash-hit oratorio *Belshazzar's Feast* (a BBC commission first performed in Leeds in 1931). If so, it was the choral drama of *Elijah* that inspired Walton. The chorus dominates *Belshazzar's Feast*. Belshazzar himself – the sybaritic king who defiles the sacred treasures of the

captive Israelites – remains a shameful anti-hero, who learns of God's wrath when he sees a hand writing on the palace wall: 'Thou art weighed in the balance and found wanting.' Walton's chilling musical effects underline Belshazzar's terror – spectral *sul ponticello* strings, harp tremolos, muffled subterranean thuds from piano and bass drum, hushed gong strokes and clicking castanets. But Belshazzar himself has no great solos. The prophet Daniel, who provides the interpretation of the writing on the wall, makes no appearance. The story is everything, its personalities mere puppets.

Where Walton assembles huge choral and orchestral forces, Benjamin Britten, in his Canticle No. 2, *Abraham and Isaac* (1952), is content with two voices and a piano. But then it is arguable that subtlety is more necessary in a setting of this strange, disturbing fable. God has fulfilled his promise to Abraham and granted him a son in old

age – the son that will make him patriarch of the Children of Israel. Then, alarmingly, God seems to change his mind and demand the boy Isaac as a sacrifice. Some believers have seen Abraham as a hero of faith, prepared even to slay his son in obedience to God; the 19th-century Danish thinker Søren Kierkegaard felt that Abraham knew in his heart that God could not want such a sacrifice of him. Britten, however, was drawn to the story by the image that obsessed him throughout his adult life: that of innocence under threat. The sparing of 'innocent' Isaac is celebrated in the beautiful final section of *Abraham and Isaac*. But Britten returned to this theme – and to some of its music – in the Offertorium of his *War Requiem* (premiered in Coventry Cathedral in 1962), where the image of deliverance is now re-framed with lacerating irony as, in Wilfred Owen's words, 'the old man ... slew his son – and half the seed of Europe, one by one'. Igor Stravinsky's setting of the same story (premiered in Jerusalem in 1964) is more enigmatic. 'I began to compose *Abraham and Isaac*,' he tells us, 'because of the attractions of the Hebrew language as sound, because of the subject and, not least, because I wanted to leave a token of my gratitude to the people of Israel, to whom the music is dedicated, for their generosity and hospitality during my tour of their country in 1962.' Here, it seems, Abraham is the symbol of Israel itself. Stravinsky's setting is less often heard

ABOVE
The Sacrifice of Isaac by
Andrea del Sarto, c1527

TOP RIGHT
Robert Helpmann as Satan
in Ninette de Valois's 1931
Vic-Wells Ballet production
of Vaughan Williams's *Job*

than Britten's, yet the Russian counted it as one of his 'best' works. This year's Proms offer a good opportunity to compare and contrast the two.

Where the texts of Stravinsky's and Britten's works include no criticism – direct or implied – of God or Abraham's actions, the dramatic scenario of Ralph Vaughan Williams's *Job* does. Like the biblical text and the William Blake engravings that inspired it, Vaughan Williams's 1930 'masque for dancing' (he himself always refused to call it a ballet) ends with God vindicated and Job restored to health and happiness after dreadful suffering. But there is a moment of terrifying doubt: Job has a vision of Satan seated on God's throne. A thunderous *fortissimo* registers Job's horror. It's as remarkable in its way as the famous surprise *fortissimo* at the words 'And there was light!' in Haydn's Handel-inspired oratorio *The Creation* (premiered in Vienna in 1798). In *Job*, however, the effect is reversed. If God himself is the flawless, omnipotent 'hero' of Haydn's *Creation*, Vaughan Williams's *Job* allows the possibility

that the idea of 'God' has its dark side, as do Blake's illustrations.

There is nothing ambiguous, however, about Handel's God in his 1739 oratorio *Israel in Egypt*. Nor does he leave us in any doubt who the hero is this time: not a striving, flawed individual as in *Samson*, but a whole people: the Children of Israel, saved from slavery in Egypt and delivered to the Promised Land. The chorus is as much centre stage here as the tenor soloist is in *Samson*. Some of *Israel in Egypt*'s earliest English admirers found a direct parallel with the destiny of their own nation. A writer to the *London Daily Post* heard the message that 'Protestant, free, virtuous, united, Christian England need little fear, at any time hereafter, the whole Force of slavish, bigotted, united, unchristian Popery, risen up against her should such a conjecture ever hereafter happen'. We may draw different conclusions today. The miracle is that, in a very different England, we can still be moved and uplifted by Handel's re-creation of this ancient story.

Old Testament Heroes at the Proms

Britten	Abraham and Isaac	PCM 7
Handel	Israel in Egypt	Prom 6
	Samson	Prom 66
Haydn	The Creation	Prom 2
Mendelssohn	Elijah	Prom 56
Nielsen	Saul & David –	
	Preludes, Acts 2 & 4	Prom 35
Saint-Saëns	Samson & Delilah	
	– extract	Prom 3
Stravinsky	Abraham and Isaac	Prom 58
Vaughan Williams		
	Job	Prom 17
Walton	Belshazzar's Feast	Prom 1

If God himself is the flawless, omnipotent 'hero' of Haydn's *Creation*, Vaughan Williams's *Job* allows the possibility that the idea of 'God' has its dark side …

DECODERS WANTED.

As an RAF musician, your one advantage will be to decipher codes that even some of our top signal operators are baffled by. We are currently looking for single-reed woodwind instrumentalists, bassoonists and percussionists. So if you're aged between 17-29 and play the clarinet, bassoon or a percussion instrument to a professional standard and have always dreamt of playing for your country, just drop a note to: Squadron Leader Dave Compton, Director of Music, HQ Music Services, RAF Uxbridge, Middlesex UB10 0RZ. Tel 01895 237144 ext. 6391. Or visit us at www.rafmusic.co.uk

BPM02

Music by Eric Coates © 1954 Chappell Music Limited, Warner/Chappell Music Limited, London W5 8BS. Reproduced by kind permission of IMP Ltd.

Music fit for a queen

Martin Neary, former Organist & Master of the Choristers at Westminster Abbey, sang as one of the children of Her Majesty's Chapels Royal at the 1953 Coronation. As the Queen celebrates her Golden Jubilee, he chronicles the music that has accompanied the crowning of Britain's monarchs through the ages

For over 1,000 years, since Edgar was crowned in Westminster Abbey in 973, the basic structure of the Coronation service has survived virtually unchanged. Music has played an increasingly important role since the earliest services, although the 'many anthemys i-sang by note', mentioned as sung at the Coronation of Henry VI, were not anthems in the modern sense of the word, but were probably portions of psalms sung to plainchant. Following the Reformation much new music was composed, and by the time of the Coronation of James I in 1603, more elaborate settings had begun to appear. One of these was Orlando Gibbons's wonderfully expressive *Te Deum*, which was chosen (in preference to the setting by Henry Purcell) for the Coronation of George II in 1727. By then, following the lead given in 1661 by Charles II and, above all, thanks to the genius of Handel, the ceremony had become a veritable musical feast.

Although today we tend to associate Coronation music with what is played and sung inside the Abbey, the Great Procession from Westminster Hall, which lapsed after 1821, always had musical accompaniment. In 1189, Richard I was led to the church 'with an ordered procession and triumphal chanting', while (as can be heard in the King's Consort's reconstruction of the Coronation of George II) there were a host of drummers in 1727. This all made for a great spectacle, which later seems to have got somewhat out of hand, causing Horace Walpole in 1761 to describe George IV's Coronation as a 'puppet show'!

This 'concert' element went largely unchecked until 1902, when, thanks principally to Armitage Robinson, the Dean of Westminster, the liturgical and theatrical elements were brought closer together. A striking example is Hubert Parry's setting of Psalm 122, the opening words of which – 'I was glad' – had been sung at the entrance of the Sovereign since 1661. For Edward VII, Parry had the inspired idea of incorporating the cries of 'Vivat rex!' ('Long live the king!') into his anthem. The new arrangement worked so well musically and liturgically that it has been used at every Coronation since.

By courtesy of the National Portrait Gallery, London (left & above)   Camera Press London (right)

LEFT
King George II in his Coronation robes (with a view of Westminster Abbey in the background): official portrait, c1727, from the studio of Charles Jervas

RIGHT
The Coronation of Queen Elizabeth II on 2 June 1953: Geoffrey Fisher, Archbishop of Canterbury, is seen holding aloft the Crown of St Edward before placing it reverently upon the Queen's head – 'at the sight whereof,' states the official Form and Order of Service, 'the people, with loud and repeated shouts, shall cry: God save the Queen!'

ABOVE
George Frideric Handel: portrait, c1727, attributed to Balthasar Denner. Handel's music has been heard at every Coronation since George II's

The Vivats go back at least to 1685, when Sandford recorded that the 40 King's Scholars of Westminster School, being placed in a Gallery 'adjoyning to the Great organ loft, Entertained Her Majesty (and then His Majesty) with this short prayer of salutation'. The timing in the Parry arrangement is crucial, and in 1953, from my place near the front of the South Gallery, east of the organ screen, I could see the Queen enter the Quire at the very moment the Vivats began.

Zadok the Priest, or rather its Latin usage *Unxerunt Salomonem*, dates from as early as the Coronation of Edgar. In 1661 the plainchant was discarded in favour of Henry Lawes's short version, which included cornets and sackbuts. Interesting enough in its historical context, Lawes's anthem suffered the fate of being succeeded by Handel's Coronation Anthems of 1727. In 1685 both John Blow and Henry Purcell had respectively written superb instrumental accompaniments in *God Spake Sometime in Visions* and *My Heart Is Inditing*, but Handel's use of the Abbey's acoustic in the opening prelude to *Zadok*, before the choir's jubilant entry, is second to none.

Before the Anointing a direct musical link with medieval Coronations has been maintained by the singing of the ancient plainsong hymn, *Veni Creator Spiritus* ('Come, Holy Ghost'). At the Coronations of George VI and Elizabeth II, there was further recognition of our rich musical heritage in the inclusion during the Homage of several short anthems from the 'Golden Age' of English cathedral music.

For me, however, as a young chorister, the musical highlight of the 1953 service was William Walton's thrillingly orchestrated *Coronation Te Deum*. Walton used all the forces at his disposal – the State Trumpeters from Kneller Hall, two semi-choruses, full orchestra, the organ (which was given a brilliant antiphonal solo part), not to mention a huge group of singers. These included, for the first time, a few sopranos and contraltos (albeit only from the 'Dominions'). I later learnt that both the Archbishop of Canterbury and Sir William McKie, the Director of Music, considered the presence of the 20 ladies to have been a mistake and said, 'It will not happen again'!

Another 1953 innovation, which surprisingly caused the Archbishop some misgiving, was the congregational singing of Vaughan Williams's *Old Hundredth*. It was RVW who had the idea, having declined to compose a new *Te Deum* or any other large-scale work. Never before in the course of the two-hour Coronation ceremony, apart from the singing of the National Anthem (not introduced, incidentally, until 1838) and the *Veni Creator*, had the congregation had a chance to sing a hymn. Yet His Grace remained unconvinced, possibly because the unfamiliarity of the arrangement left some members of the public uncertain when to come in. Congregations are still sometimes tempted to join in during the organ

37

playover, but this superb arrangement has long since earned its pre-eminent place on such occasions.

Over the years the music heard at Coronations has been a barometer of the tastes, and sometimes the prejudices, of each period. Several of the commissioned works have not really stood the test of time; certain texts inspired composers more than others. But is there another country in the world that can boast music of such variety and inspiration for these great events – be they exquisite miniatures such as Vaughan Williams's *O Taste and See*, Handel's *Zadok the Priest*, Stanford's inspired *Coronation Gloria* or the rousing marches of Elgar and Walton? The 1953 Coronation was in fact particularly rich musically, spawning not just Walton's *Orb and Sceptre* march and *Te Deum* for the service itself but Britten's Coronation opera *Gloriana*, as well as the Aldeburgh-inspired *Variations on an Elizabethan Theme (Sellinger's Round)* co-composed by Britten, Walton, Tippett and others, and the even more collaborative 10-composer collection of unaccompanied choruses *A Garland for the Queen*, modelled on Thomas Morley's 1601 set of tributes to Elizabeth I, *The Triumphs of Oriana*.

It will be fascinating to see if, at future services, new texts are included or whether any of those now discarded are restored. Of the latter, could one be the *Laudes regiae* – 'Christus vincit, Christus regnat, Christus imperat' ('Christ conquers, Christ reigns, Christ

rules') – sung at the crowning of Matilda in 1068 and then regularly until the late 14th century? The latter part of the text, with the invocation of the saints, might make its revival controversial, but there is a wonderfully effective setting of the opening words by the contemporary Scottish composer James MacMillan.

Certain settings of Coronation music are surely sacrosanct, but each generation must speak of itself, and reflect the spirit of its own age, as well as its rich inheritance. Whatever the changes, may there be many more *Triumphs of Oriana* to come.

Royal music at the Proms

Prom 9	The Triumphs of Oriana (extracts); The Oriana Collection
Prom 32	Music for the Coronation of King George II
Prom 34	Variations on an Elizabethan Theme (Sellinger's Round)
Prom 73	Walton: Anniversary Fanfare; Orb and Sceptre Parry: I Was Glad
PCM 8	A Garland for the Queen (extracts); Choral Songs in Honour of Queen Victoria; Britten: Choral Dances from 'Gloriana'

RIGHT
Queen Elizabeth II in her Coronation robes (against a background of Henry VII's Chapel in Westminster Abbey): official 1953 press photograph by Cecil Beaton

RIGHT
The seven poets and seven composers of *The Oriana Collection* (left to right in vertical pairs):
Grace Nichols/Joe Duddell;
U. A. Fanthorpe/
Howard Goodall;
Ian Sinclair/John Harle;
Jo Shapcott/John McCabe;
Simon Armitage/
Dominic Muldowney;
Andrew Motion/Jocelyn Pook;
Kathleen Jamie/Joby Talbot

The Oriana Collection

Andrew Motion, the Poet Laureate, introduces the King'singers' Golden Jubilee commission – a modern pairing of poets and composers inspired by a 17th-century Elizabethan model

BELOW
Title-page of the original *Triumphs of Oriana*, published by Thomas Morley in 1601

RIGHT
Queen Elizabeth I:
the 'portrait with the ermine' by Nicholas Hilliard (1585)

In December 2000 the King'singers wrote to me out of the blue, reminding me that they'd recently recorded the complete *Triumphs of Oriana* – the 25 madrigals compiled by Thomas Morley in 1601, and dedicated to Queen Elizabeth I – and saying that they were interested in creating and performing a contemporary response, to coincide with the Golden Jubilee of our present Queen. If they supplied the composers, would I match them to suitable and sympathetic poets? They didn't want pieces which concentrated on the monarchy as such, but which evoked aspects of our age, and of the past 50 years.

It was a delightful commission, especially since it offered a chance to measure differences as well as establish continuities. Differences of language and cultural identity; continuities of organisation and enterprise. It wasn't difficult to think of poets who were especially interested in such things. The question of 'who we are' has quite properly become a major preoccupation of our times, and is reflected in the range of backgrounds and contexts, as well as in the actual voices, of the poets I approached.

Which is not to say that the new *Oriana Collection* is explicitly didactic. The seven poets, and their composers, are as expert at giving pleasure as they are at making sense. Their collaborations are a celebration, as well as a challenge to our received ideas – a celebration of this anniversary, of our changed and changing society, and of the central role that art of every kind plays in our lives.

The Oriana Collection
Prom 9   Thursday 25 July, 10.00pm

BBC *Symphony* Orchestra

Leonard Slatkin Chief Conductor

2002-2003 Season

A season of outstanding concerts at the Barbican
under Chief Conductor Leonard Slatkin

Season highlights

- **Prokofiev Symphony Cycle** All seven symphonies

- **Composer Portraits** Oliver Knussen and Alberto Ginastera

- **Kaija Saariaho** *L'amour de loin**
  The UK premiere of this opera, described by the New York
  Times as a 'lyrical masterpiece' and starring Gerald Finley,
  Lili Paasikivi and Dawn Upshaw

- **Wagner** *Tristan und Isolde*
  The complete opera over three evenings with a star-studded
  cast including Christine Brewer and John Treleaven

- **Mark-Anthony Turnage** The January Composer Weekend
  focuses on the music and influences of the BBC Symphony
  Orchestra's Associate Composer

- **John Adams** *El Niño**
  Adams conducts the UK premiere of his oratorio with
  soloists including Dawn Upshaw and Willard White

- **Premieres** New music by Simon Bainbridge, Peter Eötvös,
  György Kurtág, Magnus Lindberg and Einojuhani Rautavaara

A magnificent roll-call of artists including
John Adams, Joshua Bell, Paavo Berglund, Ian Bostridge,
Christine Brewer, Sir Andrew Davis, Rebecca Evans, Gerald Finley,
Oliver Knussen, Christopher Maltman, Vadim Repin, Jukka-Pekka Saraste,
Vassily Sinaisky, Leonard Slatkin, Dawn Upshaw

Tickets £16 £12 £8

Become a BBC Symphony Orchestra subscriber
and save money on ticket prices.

Call the Barbican Box Office on 020 7638 8891 for
a free season brochure with full details of all concerts.
Brochure and tickets available in June.

* Different ticket prices will apply

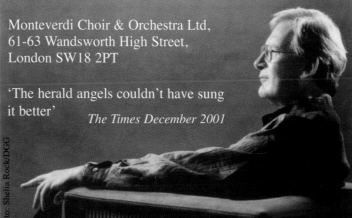

Proms commissions and premieres

Besides this year's two multi-composer projects – *The Oriana Collection* and the *Bright Cecilia Variations* (see pages 39 and 46) – this year's Proms boast 10 other premieres, including four BBC commissions. David Threasher talked to their composers

Julian Anderson (b. 1967)
Imagin'd Corners
London premiere • Prom 70

Julian Anderson's first work as Composer-in-Association to the City of Birmingham Symphony Orchestra takes its title from one of John Donne's Holy Sonnets, 'At the round earth's imagin'd corners'. Having been impressed by the CBSO's horn section, he wanted to write a work in which they were specifically featured and conceived this piece in which four of the five horn soloists are mobile, moving about the stage and even playing from the wings. This antiphonal use of forces creates, in Anderson's words, 'a Mahlerian evocation of space and distance, in the mind, as well as in physical reality'. He also harks back to the horn's hunting associations, using the rustic sound of the bare harmonic series alongside the more refined sounds offered by the valve horn. 'What I like about the horn tuning,' he says, 'is that it's rough, in the sense of being natural. The contrasts in terms of character are fairly sharp. The piece tries to bring out the various characters of horn-playing – and those characters transfer themselves to the orchestra when the horns aren't playing. But my use of microtones is to do with harmonic coherence – not so they sound out of tune!'

Simon Bainbridge (b. 1952)
Chant
London premiere • Prom 61

Simon Bainbridge's *Chant* was composed for the BBC Philharmonic and the BBC Singers and premiered by them under Harry Christophers at York Minster in November 1999, as part of the BBC's *Sounding the Millennium* festival. In many ways, the majesty of the Minster itself was as much a stimulus to Bainbridge as the prospect of composing for two of the country's leading ensembles. 'I have often found that writing a piece for a specific acoustic and architectural space can provide a composer with enough initial aural stimuli to set off a torrent of musical ideas,' he says. After a visit to the Minster, he adds, 'I came away with the beginnings of a strange "antiphonal" sound-world that I felt would suit the grandeur of this magnificent building.' Bainbridge uses a monodic hymn by Hildegard of Bingen as his raw material, dispersing it between the voices and relaying their lines to speakers set around the space. The Royal Albert Hall should rise splendidly to the challenge of recreating the veiled resonance of Bainbridge's unique sound-world.

Marc-André Dalbavie (b. 1961)
Color
UK premiere • Prom 63

'What I wanted to do was an atonal piece with tonal chords,' says Marc-André Dalbavie of his new work, *Color*, which was composed for Christoph Eschenbach and the Orchestre de Paris, and premiered by them in New York in January. Dalbavie emerged from the so-called Spectralist school that developed in France in the 1970s and 1980s around such composers as Tristan Murail and the late Gérard Grisey, whose intention was to base their music on the harmonic spectra of sounds. Dalbavie has also experimented with spatial music – seating the orchestra around the audience, for example. *Color*, though, opts for a more traditional seating plan, but features ranks of percussion that shimmer and undulate throughout the work. 'It's a cycle of melodies of colour from the 14th century, like a circle, not like a forward trajectory,' he explains. His current projects include a work for the Birmingham Contemporary Music Group and one to mark Franz Welser-Möst's debut as Music Director of the Cleveland Orchestra later this year.

John Harle (b. 1956)
The Little Death Machine
World premiere • Prom 24

John Harle is already well known to Proms audiences both as a saxophonist – he gave the controversial premiere of Sir Harrison Birtwistle's *Panic* at the Last Night of the 1995 Proms – and as a composer – his one-act opera *Angel Magick* was an innovatory event four years ago. This season, he appears as both soloist and composer in the world premiere of his latest work, *The Little Death Machine*, which he describes as 'a short concerto for saxophone with chamber orchestra'. But it goes further than that, as Harle explains: 'Jake and Dino Chapman's highly sexually-charged sculpture (of a similar title) at Tate Modern set this particular machine in motion.' As the machine gets into its rhythm, the music 'heads for home with angular repetitive lines of increasing vigour with virtuoso playing required from the orchestra and the saxophonist, who ends up on the little-used sopranino saxophone, a wild instrument with a sound of penetrative intensity – a wailing Celtic pipe.'
See also 'The Oriana Collection', page 39

Per Nørgård (b. 1932)
Symphony No. 6
UK premiere • Prom 15

The unfolding Sibelian lyricism and infinite systems of Per Nørgård make a belated Proms debut with the Danish composer's most recent symphony, completed three years ago, and subtitled 'At the End of the Day'. Connected thematically to his orchestral work *Terrains vagues*, a BBC commission premiered by the BBC Symphony Orchestra last year, the Sixth Symphony was conceived to be played in the first days of the new millennium; the subtitle not only refers to the change of the calendar, but also reminds us, with a touch of irony, that the end is never final – something always remains. The most outwardly optimistic and rhythmically infectious – if unpredictable and dramatic – of his symphonies, this latest reflects Nørgård's untiring curiosity and his ability constantly to evolve his compositional style, even as he enters his eighth decade.

BBC COMMISSION
Anthony Payne (b. 1936)
Visions and Journeys
World premiere • Prom 22

Anthony Payne is probably best known for his work elaborating the sketches of Elgar's unfinished Third Symphony – a labour of love that spanned more than a quarter of a century. But it would be wrong to see Elgar's influence as pervading Payne's own work as a composer, despite his love of Elgar and the English music of the early 20th century. His new work – his first major orchestral piece since the completion of Elgar's Third – is, like his two previous Proms commissions, a 25-minute tone poem, which he sees as a single-movement symphony in the manner of the Seventh Symphony of Sibelius, another composer whom Payne admires deeply. *Visions and Journeys* is not programmatic as such, he says, but 'the journeys are the dynamic, forward-moving music in the piece – motoric images, like trains; while the visions are more static, maybe things seen along the way'.
See also 'Hail once more, bright Cecilia!', page 46

BBC COMMISSION
Joseph Phibbs (b. 1974)
La noche arrolladora
World premiere • PCM 3

Joseph Phibbs owes his strong compositional voice to his refusal to follow fashion: 'I'm not keen on the idea of musical ideologies or camps; to me the best music should be full of strong, imaginative ideas that are developed in compelling ways.' His distinctive style has led to commissions from the London Sinfonietta, the Schubert Ensemble and, last year, the BBC Symphony Orchestra, and his music has been championed in Europe and the Far East by such figures as Leonard Slatkin and George Benjamin. Phibbs insists his new work for the English Chamber Orchestra Ensemble is not a concerto, but 'demonstrates the various ways in which the highly distinctive sound of the harpsichord may be both interwoven within a small chamber group and at other points used to stand out as an entirely isolated, unrelated part of the ensemble. The brittle, percussive sonorities of the instrument are contrasted against soft, sustained lines, while fast antiphonal exchanges explore the wide range of timbres available among the players.'

Malcolm Crowthers (Harle, Nørgård, Payne)

Malcolm Crowthers (Sawer, Turnage)

BBC COMMISSION

David Sawer (b. 1961)

Piano Concerto

World premiere • Prom 5

David Sawer is no stranger to the Proms, with commissions such as *Songs of Love and War*, *Byrnan Wood* and *the greatest happiness principle* having made debuts at the Proms over the past decade or so. Last year saw the triumphant unveiling at English National Opera of his powerful and lyrical *From Morning to Midnight*, an Expressionistic 'amorality play' featuring impulsive felony and Faustian pacts. Given that he describes himself as 'a theatre person who writes music', it is not surprising that extra-musical impulses have provided the inspiration for much of Sawer's work outside the theatre, from contemporary art to photographs of the Wright Brothers' maiden flight. The Piano Concerto traces a journey of sorts: the soloist is initially pitted in conflict with the orchestra, in what Sawer calls 'a scenario of flight and pursuit', but is later reconciled with the orchestra – 'integrated into its landscape'. The soloist will be Rolf Hind, a pianist much admired by Sawer for 'his fantastic rhythmic precision and his quiet poetry'. *See also 'Hail once more, bright Cecilia!', page 46*

Roberto Sierra (b. 1953)

Fandangos

UK premiere • Prom 1

The Spanish flavour of this season's First-Night fiesta is enhanced by the UK premiere of *Fandangos* by Puerto Rico-born Roberto Sierra. Leonard Slatkin, the BBC Symphony Orchestra's Chief Conductor, commissioned the work and premiered it with his other band, the National Symphony Orchestra of Washington DC, in February last year. 'I knew immediately after our first reading of *Fandangos* that every orchestra will want to do this piece – and soon!' enthuses Slatkin. Sierra's music is notable for his vibrant and percussive orchestration, and his appropriation of Latin-American popular styles, which he cunningly stirs in the melting pot with aspects of European modernism. *Fandangos* was 'born out of my desire to compose a work based on the Fandango by Padre Antonio Soler,' he explains. 'This keyboard work by the 18th-century Spanish composer serves as a frame for my orchestral work. I also incorporated elements from Scarlatti and Boccherini, with my own Baroque machinations – hence the plural in the title.' Reviews of the premiere called it 'sultry and seductive, bright and fanciful'; as Sierra says, 'I wanted to make this piece into a brilliant *tour de force* for the orchestra.'

BBC COMMISSION

Mark-Anthony Turnage (b. 1960)

New work

World premiere • Prom 17

Mark-Anthony Turnage continues to write to the strengths of the BBC Symphony Orchestra, of which he has been Associate Composer since autumn 2000. His new work for the orchestra forms the centrepiece to a triptych of works displaying the virtuosity of the players for whom he has so much admiration. *A Quick Blast*, the first panel, gave the orchestra's wind players a starring role, while the third panel will put the string section in the limelight. This central section – the longest of the panels, but no less compact and intense – is described by Turnage as a concerto for orchestra. He turns the spotlight on pairs of instruments in turn, presenting them in a series of lamenting, keening duets accompanied by the rest of the players, treating the orchestra almost like a big band, with the duettists stepping out in turn to weave their improvisatory-sounding dialogues. Many of Turnage's works take poems or paintings as their starting-point, but he says this one is based more on a feeling – which may give a clue to its lyrical, singing lines.

Hail once more, bright Cecilia!

Colin Matthews introduces *BBC Music Magazine*'s 10th-anniversary commission – a new collaborative set of Purcell variations inspired by a Coronation Year model

Collaborative variations have a long history. Perhaps the most famous are the 50 commissioned from his contemporaries (including the young Schubert and a very young Liszt) by Anton Diabelli in 1819, although their fame lies principally in Beethoven's refusal to play the game and subsequent writing of his own solo set of 33.

A more recent example, which you can hear in this year's season (Prom 34), is the set of variations on *Sellinger's Round* commissioned by Britten for the 1953 Aldeburgh Festival, with contributions from Lennox Berkeley, Imogen Holst, Arthur Oldham, Humphrey Searle, Michael Tippett, William Walton and Britten himself.

The fact that such collaborations tend to be linked to particular events, coupled with their emphasis on stylistic variety, makes it hard for them to enter the repertoire. Are composers deterred therefore by being asked to write something that by its very nature may get only a handful of performances? In this case, emphatically not – the willingness to collaborate has been remarkable.

This is entirely due to the influence and charm of Helen Wallace, Editor of *BBC Music Magazine*, who conceived the idea of *Bright Cecilia* to mark the magazine's 10th anniversary. Having spent so long asking contributors, often composers, to write about music, she felt that this was a chance to turn the tables and ask composers to write music. Although she asked my advice on how the project might work, the choice of composers was ultimately hers – a daunting task to narrow down to eight a field where many more had equal claim. The list was deliberately international, and I'm delighted that Lukas Foss, Magnus Lindberg, Poul Ruders and Michael Torke all agreed to join a British contingent comprising Anthony Payne, David Sawer, Judith Weir and myself.

Hers too was the choice of theme, from Purcell's 1692 *Ode to St Cecilia*, and its evocative aria 'Thou tun'st this world', of which she writes, 'Purcell sets this grand claim to a graceful, unassuming melody, with characteristically eccentric twists and turns – corners I hoped would prove provocative.'

Provocative music for the Last Night of the Proms? We can only wait and see: at the time of writing, none of the variations had yet been composed!

Bright Cecilia: Variations on a Theme by Purcell
Prom 73 Saturday 14 September, 7.30pm

ABOVE
The eight composers of
Bright Cecilia (top to bottom):
Lukas Foss, Magnus Lindberg,
Colin Matthews,
Anthony Payne,
Poul Ruders, David Sawer,
Michael Torke, Judith Weir

LEFT
The Henry Wood memorial window
in St Sepulchre, High Holborn,
with St Cecilia pictured above,
Henry Wood and Purcell bottom right

Malcolm Crowthers (St Cecilia window, Matthews, Payne, Sawer) Boosey & Hawkes (Foss) Maarit Kytöharju/Finnish Music Information Centre (Lindberg) Suste Bonnen (Ruders) Joanna Eldredge Morrissey (Torke) Suzanne Jansen (Weir)

barbican

*'The refurbished auditorium is a revelation...
the new sense of immediacy and detail is compelling,
and the physicality of the sound genuinely exciting'*

THE GUARDIAN

mostly MOZART 11 JULY – 3 AUGUST 2002

Great Performers
2002·2003

Over four weekends London's first Mostly Mozart festival offers concerts, films, talks and special events.

The Barbican's international classical music series returns this autumn.

Mostly Mozart features:

Academy of St Martin in the Fields
Garsington Opera's London debut
Freddy Kempf
Emma Bell
Louis Lortie
Leila Josefowicz
Ingmar Bergman's *The Magic Flute*

Artists include:

Maxim Vengerov | Yo-Yo Ma
San Francisco Symphony Orchestra
Michael Tilson-Thomas
Mikhail Pletnev | Andreas Scholl
Les Arts Florissants | English National Opera
Vladimir Ashkenazy | Sir Simon Rattle
Kirov Opera Orchestra

Box Office
020 7638 8891 (bkg fee)
www.barbican.org.uk

For free brochures with full details of these concerts call the Barbican Box Office on **020 7638 8891** or email **mostlymozart@barbican.org.uk** or **greatperformers@barbican.org.uk** (quoting 'Proms Guide')

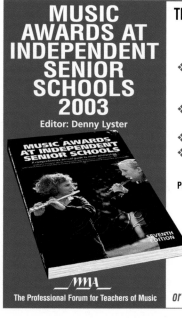

BBC SINGERS

Chief Conductor: Stephen Cleobury
Principal Guest Conductor: Bob Chilcott
Associate Composer: Edward Cowie

BBC SINGERS

2002 FESTIVAL APPEARANCES INCLUDE ALDEBURGH, CHELTENHAM, HUDDERSFIELD, LUCERNE, SPITALFIELDS AND THE BBC PROMS

The magnificent BBC Singers

The Daily Telegraph

The BBC Singers dazzled the audience with their collective sound and superb technical skills

Tygodnik Powszechny (Warsaw)

A stunning recital given by the BBC Singers

Yorkshire Post

GERALD PLACE

For more information about forthcoming
concerts, join the BBC Singers free mailing list
Tel: 020 7765 1862   Email: singers@bbc.co.uk   www.bbc.co.uk/singers

BBC RADIO 3 90-93FM

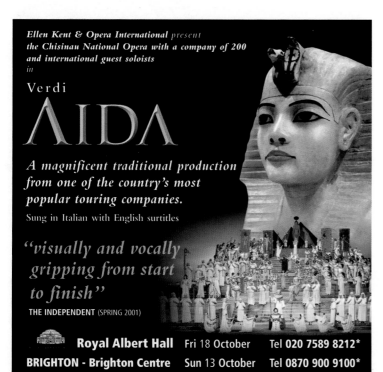

William Walton (1902–83)

Malcolm Hayes charts the composer's rapid rise from
Lancashire choirboy to Britain's unofficial Composer Laureate

E ver since its premiere at the 1931
Leeds Festival, *Belshazzar's Feast*
has been one of the works for
which its composer's name is most
admired and loved throughout the
English-speaking world. We tend to
think of this spectacularly unorthodox
oratorio as quintessential Walton. In
many ways of course it is, with its
tearing rhythmic energy, its fusion of
the English choral tradition with the
roguish sound-world of 1920s jazz, and
its virtuoso craftsmanship, so brilliantly
calculated and paced.

All this reflects the complex
background that had been the making
of Walton as an artist. He was born in
the Lancashire mill-town of Oldham,
where he sang in choirs conducted by
his father, and from where he escaped –
via his years first as a chorister, then as
an undergraduate, at Oxford's Christ
Church College – to a precarious
composer's life in London. There he
lived as a kind of adopted brother to
Edith, Osbert and Sacheverell Sitwell
in the family's Chelsea home.

Walton's progress from those
beginnings towards the triumph of
Belshazzar's Feast (or, as he later liked
to call it, 'Belli's Binge') might seem to
have a kind of retrospective inevitability.

In fact it had more to do with skilful
opportunism and sheer luck. If just a
few events of those formative years had
not happened, Walton would probably
have become a quite different composer.
The clues are in *Façade*.

The first of what were to be several
versions of this dazzling 'Entertainment'
for reciter and chamber group was
performed in the Sitwells' house (with
Edith declaiming her verses from behind
a screen through a megaphone) when
the composer was not yet 20. The work
soon created a useful *succès de scandale*,
but it was never going to earn Walton
much of a living. '*Façade*? It *keeps* me,'
he said delightedly in a BBC television
interview many years later. But he was
referring to the two 'easy listening'
orchestral suites he made from it –
not to the sharply unconventional
original work, in which Sitwell's
rhythmical, semi-abstract poems are
spoken above an accompaniment that
is a phenomenon of wry invention and
technical assurance. *Façade*'s tone was
far closer to the contemporary Paris of
Milhaud, Poulenc, Satie and company
(with a whiff of Schoenberg's *Pierrot
lunaire*) than to an English musical
scene centred round Elgar, Holst and
Vaughan Williams.

But Walton soon seems to have
decided that he would rather be a
successful composer for his home
market than be marginalised as a rarely
performed modernist. It was his bright
and breezy overture *Portsmouth Point*
(1925) that began to secure him the first
real stages of popular success. From
then on, a sequence of masterworks
blended striking individuality,
superlative technique and a shrewd ear
for what Walton's audiences would be
reasonably sure to like.

Even so, without the support of
the newly founded BBC, Walton might
have found making the necessary
headway more difficult. The Viola
Concerto, with its characteristic fusion
of snappy rhythmic flair and poignant,
yet astringent lyricism (you can feel the
sun of Walton's beloved Italy glowing
through the orchestral scoring), was
premiered at a Queen's Hall Prom in
October 1929. *Belshazzar's Feast* began

LEFT
William Walton (Capri, 1948):
portrait by Michael Ayrton

RIGHT
Walton *(second right)* with
Osbert, Edith and Sacheverell
Sitwell and co-reciter Neil
Porter (plus megaphone) at a
1926 performance of *Façade*

National Portrait Gallery, London/© Estate of Michael Ayrton (left) Courtesy of William Walton Archives (right)

life as a BBC commission that year. So, many years later, did the opera *Troilus and Cressida*, the first major work Walton completed after moving to the island of Ischia in the Bay of Naples. And the explosively intense, and long delayed, First Symphony was first heard complete when the BBC Symphony Orchestra played it at the Queen's Hall under Hamilton Harty in 1935.

Yet there are few passages in any of these works that truly sound as if they were written by the composer of *Façade*. And who could have foreseen that the creator of that deliciously irreverent early masterpiece would inherit Elgar's mantle as the nation's unofficial Composer Laureate for state occasions? Walton's march *Crown Imperial* – yet another BBC commission, written for the coronation of King George VI in 1937 – was the first in a line of ceremonial works that included *Orb and Sceptre* and the *Coronation Te Deum*, both for Queen Elizabeth II's coronation in 1953. During the Second World War, besides a number of fine film scores, Walton wrote the incidental music for another BBC project, Louis MacNeice's radio play *Christopher Columbus*. At its broadcast in 1942, the title-role was taken by Laurence Olivier; and when Olivier directed and starred in his film version of *Henry V*, he readily admitted that its great success owed much to Walton's now classic score.

There is so much more to Walton's output, too, than the deservedly famous masterpieces. In 1971, with Malcolm

Arnold's assistance, he arranged his beautiful String Quartet in A minor of 1945 for string orchestra, so that it now has a happy double life as the Sonata for Strings. *The Twelve*, a setting of a W. H. Auden text on the lives of the Apostles, was written in 1965 for Christ Church Cathedral Choir, in which Walton had sung as a boy; he later arranged its organ accompaniment for orchestra, turning the church anthem into a vivid miniature cantata. Indeed his early grounding in choral music had never left him. The haunting *Set Me as a Seal upon Thine Heart* (1938) and *Where Does the Uttered Music Go?* (first sung in 1946, at the unveiling of a memorial window to Proms founder-conductor Henry Wood in St Sepulchre's Church, High Holborn) are among the series of smaller choral works that were to punctuate his output at regular intervals. And yet, within six years of singing in his own *Drop, Drop, Slow Tears* at Christ Church at Easter 1916, aged just 14, Walton was conducting the first performance of *Façade* before a startled audience in the Sitwell family's Chelsea drawing-room. Perhaps no other young composer's development has ever been quite so rapid. Or quite so unpredictable.

RIGHT
Laurence Olivier as Henry V: he called Walton's score 'the most wonderful I've ever heard for a film'

Walton at the Proms

Prom 1	Belshazzar's Feast
Prom 11	Christopher Columbus (suite, arr. C. Palmer)
Prom 25	Viola Concerto
Prom 34	Variations on an Elizabethan Theme (Sellinger's Round)
Prom 40	Sonata for Strings
Prom 60	Symphony No. 1
Prom 61	The Twelve
Prom 73	Anniversary Fanfare; Orb and Sceptre; Henry V (suite, arr. Sargent)
PCM 1	Façade
PCM 8	A Litany; Set Me as a Seal upon Thine Heart; Where Does the Uttered Music Go?

B·B·C
Symphony Concert

WILLIAM WALTON

SYMPHONY No.1

FIRST PERFORMANCE OF THE COMPLETE WORK

TO-NIGHT AT **8.30**
AT 8.30
IN THE QUEEN'S HALL

ABOVE
Poster for the first complete performance of Walton's First Symphony, given by the BBC Symphony Orchestra on 6 November 1935

Maurice Duruflé (1902–86)

Richard Langham Smith celebrates the centenary of the organist-composer whose unique harmonies captured the very essence of French liturgical music

ABOVE
Maurice Duruflé at the organ of Saint-Etienne du Mont, the Paris church *(right)* where he was organist for over 50 years

Anyone who has ever caught the tail-end of Sunday Mass at one of the classier Paris churches will know that special atmosphere as the West Doors are opened: the scent of snuffed candles mingles with an evaporating cloud of incense whose bitter-sweet pungency is matched by waves of harmonies from the *grand orgue*, perhaps shot through with fragments of plainsong pertinent to the day. The organist is probably improvising and has had years of training in the art.

It's a tradition whose lineage goes back a long way. One of its founts was the École Niedermeyer, a Parisian institution devoted to the restoration of plainsong, and to finding ways of harmonising it with ever more juicy chords. There Saint-Saëns taught Fauré (and later gave him a job at the Madeleine). At St Clothilde, on the Left Bank, Charles Tournemire succeeded César Franck as organist and became the improviser supreme in the plainsong tradition. Maurice Duruflé became Tournemire's assistant there as well as his pupil.

One of Duruflé's major legacies was to immortalise this tradition, to set it in stone. He captured all the atmosphere of Parisian liturgical practice in his celebrated *Requiem* of 1947, every section of which is based on an appropriate plainsong theme. It is inevitably compared to Fauré's – not least because, like Fauré's, it exists both in a parochial version with organ and in a concert version with orchestra.

But there were other aspects to Duruflé's art, among them his sense of colour inherited on the one hand from the less liturgical organist Louis Vierne – more interested in Naiads and other impressionist fantasies than plainchant – and on the other from his composition teacher Paul Dukas, whose class he attended alongside the young Olivier Messiaen. For while Duruflé was no doubt an excellent improviser, he was also a composer committed to the sculpting of highly-crafted forms, never satisfied in his compositions with the loose meandering of the indulgent organist. His organ pieces and delicious unaccompanied motets are testimony to this, while his reputation was that of a kind and conscientious teacher, and of a somewhat severe man.

Born in Louviers, in Normandy, he went to the choir school in Rouen before moving to Paris to study with Tournemire in 1919. At the Paris Conservatoire he won first prizes in harmony, accompaniment and organ-playing and in 1927 became assistant to Vierne at Notre-Dame before himself becoming organist at Saint-Etienne du Mont three years later. He gave the premiere of Poulenc's Organ Concerto in 1939 and enjoyed an international career as a performer until he and his wife, Marie-Madeleine, were incapacitated in a car accident in 1975.

The Paris Conservatoire sought him out as a harmony teacher above all. Hardly surprising! For his harmony, at once unique but encapsulating that atmosphere which was the essence of French religious music of the 20th century, arose from a deep understanding and a consummate skill. Its power to affect us, and to lead us towards the mystical, remains undiminished.

Duruflé at the Proms
Prom 61   Requiem
PCM 6   Prelude, Recitative
           and Variations, Op. 3

55

Oliver Knussen (born 1952)

Paul Driver salutes a prodigy-turned-Grand-Old-Man who has produced 'two of the most enchanting operas of recent decades'

ABOVE
Oliver Knussen: 50 this year

LEFT & RIGHT
Maurice Sendak's title-page illustrations for his classic children's picture-book *Where the Wild Things Are*

Oliver Knussen was a child prodigy – he conducted the London Symphony Orchestra in his own First Symphony (a brash four-movement work that still stands up) when only 15 – and in an odd sort of way has become, at 50, a prodigy Grand Old Man: a conductor revered across the globe, distinguished ex-festival director, and composer of two of the most enchanting operas of recent decades. His oeuvre is not large, his works are never overlong, but they are always brilliantly imagined, with an inner cogency that is exemplary in this age of too many -isms. His music is a gold standard for artistically inflationary times.

Minutely attentive craftsmanship was evident from the start: in his Second Symphony, a teenage score far more sophisticated than its predecessor (it doubles as an orchestral song-cycle to words by Trakl and Plath), and in such bitingly attractive chamber works as *Trumpets* for soprano and three clarinets (another Trakl setting), the vocally eloquent *Cantata* for oboe and string trio, the colourful *Ophelia Dances* for small ensemble and the headlong if foreshortened *Coursing* for large one. Knussen's style is eclectic in

origin – Musorgsky, Debussy, Berg, Carter and Bernstein are among his influences – but easily recognisable: a music of distinctive fluency and harmonic richness. The flow reflects his investigation of cinematic (Hitchcockian) pacing and editing; the harmony his watchmaker's precision in making the tiniest components fit together: a vertical slice from a Knussen score is apt to have a gem-like textural finish.

This depth of detail means that even his shortest pieces are weighty: he can pack more into a bar than many composers into a movement. But in his most outstanding achievements – the single-span Third Symphony, say, or the double-bill of fantasy operas, *Where the Wild Things Are* and *Higglety Pigglety Pop!*, each to a libretto by the children's writer-illustrator Maurice Sendak – he manages to reconcile miniaturist perfectionism with onward momentum and sheer oomph in a way that, in the case of the operas, is quite as much a part of their magic as sumptuous lyricism or fairy-tale imagery.

The strain of such an exacting compositional synthesis told on Knussen. The double-bill left him 'completely exhausted, and for two years I could hardly compose at all'.

It began to seem as though his career as one of the finest, most unfussily communicative conductors of modern music was taking over from the business of actually writing it. But starting with the clean sheet, as it were, of some unaccompanied vocal miniatures (settings of Rilke), he has produced a series of scores whose modest dimensions and conscious avoidance of 'big statement' only reaffirm, while seeking to re-evaluate, his creative premises. The four *Songs without Voices* for eight instruments, four *Whitman Settings* for soprano and orchestra, the tersely romantic Horn Concerto are works whose expressive impactedness demands, and whose charm compels, repeated listenings. As for the large-ensemble *Two Organa* (the first an arrangement of a tiny Knussen piece for music-box), their tinkling charm leaves no doubt that here is a Grand Old Man with direct access to the tingling freshness of childhood itself.

Knussen at the Proms

Prom 10 Where the Wild Things Are;
        Higglety Pigglety Pop!

© Maurice Sendak (left & right). © Betty Freeman (above)

Richard Rodgers (1902–79)

Edward Seckerson, presenter of Radio 3's *Stage & Screen*,
pays centenary tribute to a born melodist

'I have a story... I see a stage... I am standing in the orchestra pit. The lights are beginning to dim, the curtain is going up. I must have a song here with proper music. I sit down and write that music.' Just like that. Simple, really. Actually it was. Melodies came easily to Richard Rodgers; they sat naturally under his fingers. By the time they reached our ears they already seemed a part of our musical memory. As we celebrate his centenary, it's time to pull out the big statements. Here's one: Rodgers was the greatest, the most naturally gifted, the most versatile popular melodist of them all.

For more than six decades he graced the musical theatre with some of its sweetest sounds. He wrote more than 900 published songs – that's 300 up on Schubert (and with generally smarter lyrics) – and 40 Broadway musicals. With Lorenz Hart, his first enduring partnership, Rodgers perfected the sound of regret, a bitter-sweetness that owed much, as Rodgers himself once put it, to the clash between 'sentimental melody and unsentimental lyric'. With Oscar Hammerstein II came a whole new deal: an open-heartedness with stars in its eyes.

Rodgers was once asked what he had done before he began composing. 'I was a baby,' he replied. It was a jest that very nearly came back to haunt him. In the early 1920s, when times were tough, he contemplated taking a job selling baby clothes. An eleventh-hour request to compose the score for a benefit in aid of the Theatre Guild came just in the nick of time. He and Hart seized the moment and scored their first enduring hit: 'Manhattan'. 'We'll have Manhattan, the Bronx and Staten Island too.' The crafty slant-rhyme of that single couplet insinuated its way into the public consciousness. The words were sharp and calculated but the melody undercut their cleverness and gave the song a nonchalance that made it easy to sing along with. The world did. 'Manhattan' was written in 1925. Hart's cynicism was limbering up for the Great Depression. His caustic rhymes tugged away at what Cole Porter

ABOVE
Yul Brynner in *The King & I*

FAR LEFT
Richard Rodgers (at the piano)
with Oscar Hammerstein II

LEFT & RIGHT
Original publicity pictures for
*The Sound of Music, Carousel,
South Pacific* and *Oklahoma!*

once called the 'holiness' of Rodgers's tunes. The chemistry was extraordinary. Hart encouraged an edge, a playfulness in Rodgers's melodies; Rodgers, in turn, gave Hart's more capricious lyrics elegance and shape; he made them sing. Together, they were a modern-day G&S. They had wit, wisdom and countless ways of saying 'I love you' in 32 bars.

The transition from Rodgers & Hart to Rodgers & Hammerstein was as timely as any in Broadway history. At the centre of it was a play – *Green Grow the Lilacs*. Extraordinary to think now that had Larry Hart not been losing his grip on life, had Rodgers not turned to Hammerstein, or had Hammerstein turned to Jerome Kern, and so on and so forth, *Oklahoma!* might not have happened when it did and in the way that it did.

Rodgers's musical voice had really soared in the final decade of the Hart partnership. The melodies were extending their reach. Where Rodgers was going Hart couldn't go. Hammerstein, on the other hand, was already there. He believed in romance, he believed in 'the bright golden haze on the meadow'. Sceptics have said that the most original thing about *Oklahoma!* was the exclamation mark in the title, that this so-called 'breakthrough' musical was merely an elaborate variation on an old formula. But those who knew better realised that the way in which its song and dance were integrated into the very fabric of the drama was a huge advance on anything that had gone before. The play – the 'book', as it's known in the

trade – was the thing. The music gave it a reach and an exuberance hitherto unimaginable in this most popular of genres. We were suddenly a very long way from June/moon clichés.

'People Will Say We're in Love' – the key-note duet from *Oklahoma!* – is the ultimate 'play hard to get' number, the words striving but failing to belie the uplift of the melody. That melody turns on a simple but gloriously effective inversion of the opening phrase at the 'bridge' or 'release' of the song. It lends symmetry to its design, it raises the emotional stakes more than anyone can say but, like most of Rodgers's truly inspired turns of phrase, it's completely unconscious. In other words, instinct before method, before technique.

A natural melodist. Stephen Sondheim once spent a redundant hour in Rodgers's company trying to find out not why but *how* he did things. You see, we can identify what makes a Rodgers melody special or 'catchy', what it is that makes the next note inevitable the second after you hear it; we can take the melody apart and pinpoint a sequence of thirds or fourths here, a repeated pattern there, an unexpected displacement, a quirk of rhythm. But the disarmingly simple arrangement of notes that make up a great melody like 'With a Song in My Heart' (from the show he wrote with Hart in 1929 – *Spring Is Here*) cannot explain the elation we experience when we hear it. In this case we're told it can be attributed to Rodgers's first aeroplane flight. Fear of flying overcome? As a composer, yes.

There's something else, too. Melody, not harmony, leads the ear. 'A great melody,' Rodgers once said, 'implies its own harmony.' Significant words. Lesser melodies hide behind the harmony. Rodgers's melodies don't need to. You could argue that the harmony of a song like 'Something Wonderful' from *The King and I* is integral to the melody. But take it away, and what happens? It's still there. Magic? Not really.

Rodgers always played down the notion of inspiration, claiming that even a score like *Carousel* – surely his lyric masterpiece – was merely the product of hard work. But a song like 'What's the Use of Wondrin'?' has very little to do with hard work. The ache in the melody comes from somewhere deep inside, and if we knew where, we'd all be at it.

Rodgers at the Proms

Prom 37   Babes in Arms – overture;
          Victory at Sea – suite;
          Oklahoma!
Prom 73   Songs

OKLAHOMA

GRAMOPHONE
THE CLASSICAL MUSIC MAGAZINE

WE'RE AS SERIOUS ABOUT CLASSICAL MUSIC AS YOU ARE.
SEE FOR YOURSELF.

3 FREE ISSUES OF GRAMOPHONE – WORTH £11.85
WHEN YOU SUBSCRIBE BY DIRECT DEBIT

To take up this NO RISK trial offer simply complete the coupon below and we will send you your three free issues with their Editor's choice CDs. Plus, this is a risk-free offer. Should you decide that Gramophone is not for you, simply cancel and owe nothing. To subscribe, no further action is required. £9.50 will come to us after your free issues and every 3 issues thereafter.

GLYNDEBOURNE
ON TOUR
2002

G BIZET

Carmen

A new production by David McVicar,
premiered at the 2002 Festival

P TCHAIKOVSKY

Eugene Onegin

A revival of Graham Vick's production,
premiered in 1994

B BRITTEN

Albert Herring

A revival of Peter Hall's production,
premiered in 1985

PHOTOGRAPH + MIKE HOBAN

GLYNDEBOURNE	8 – 26 October
PLYMOUTH	29 October – 2 November
MILTON KEYNES	5 – 9 November
NORWICH	12 – 16 November
WOKING	19 – 23 November
STOKE-ON-TRENT	26 – 30 November
OXFORD	3 – 7 December

To join our FREE mailing list and receive full details
of the 2002 Tour please call 01273 815000
or email info@glyndebourne.com
or write to: GTO Mailing list, Freepost BR (235),
Glyndebourne, Lewes, East Sussex BN8 4BR

www.glyndebourne.com

'GLYNDEBOURNE ON TOUR . . .
A YOUTHFUL AND VIBRANT
JOURNEY' *Sunday Independent 2000*

SUPPORTED BY
PETER MOORES FOUNDATION

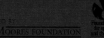

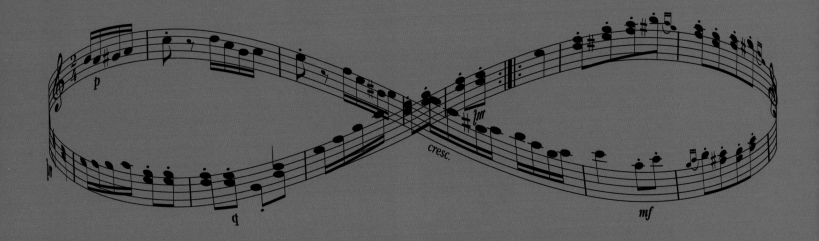

non-stop music

Dvořák • Stabat mater

Jan Smaczny explains how the Czech composer drew musical consolation from the pain of a triple family tragedy

RIGHT
Such was Dvořák's popularity in England following his UK debut conducting his *Stabat mater* at the Royal Albert Hall that his face even appeared on sets of cigarette cards

ABOVE
The title-page of the composer's manuscript score

On hearing a fellow composer criticised for being insufficiently Czech, Dvořák (with customary incisiveness) asked: 'And what is national about my *Stabat mater*?' Although the *Stabat mater* was begun early in 1876, at a time when Dvořák was adopting a much more consciously national accent, it shows us a very different composer from the one who penned such open-hearted classics as the first set of *Slavonic Dances* at almost the same time. The composer revealed in the *Stabat mater* has a rich and complex musical personality responsive to a diverse range of styles including Italian opera and aspects of Baroque music; indeed, the work reminds us that Dvořák's musical education differed very little from that enjoyed by his 18th-century Czech predecessors.

Dvořák was most likely prompted to compose the *Stabat mater* – a setting of the traditional devotional poem about the Virgin Mary's vigil at Christ's Cross – by the acute personal grief he felt at the death of his daughter Josefina in August 1875, only two days after her birth. Conceived on an epic scale hitherto unprecedented in the Czech repertoire, the work was sketched some three months later and then laid aside.

But only 18 months were to pass before Dvořák was driven back to complete the score in response to yet another family tragedy, the deaths of his remaining children Růžena and Otakar.

The indisputable greatness of the work resides in its craft and in the astonishing sincerity of its musical language. The opening movement, one of the most impressively sustained in Dvořák's entire output, seems to evoke a vast procession of humanity approaching the foot of the Cross. The music ranges broadly with hints of Italian opera, which Dvořák had imbibed richly as a viola player in Prague's first Czech theatre, while, in the anguished, falling chromatic sighs of the main motif, there is a clear debt to Baroque principles of composition. The Baroque impulse is also strong in the 'Tui nati vulnerati' section, with its Bach-like fluency, and in the stirring ritornelli of the magnificent alto aria, 'Inflammatus', an impulse Dvořák blends effortlessly with the richest romantic harmonies in its closing bars. There are many sublime moments, not least the magnificent use of the women's chorus in 'Fac ut ardeat cor meum'. There is also room for a uniquely Czech simplicity in the hymn-like 'Fac me vere' for tenor and men's chorus, which traces its roots to the traditions of the Czech village choirmaster from which Dvořák sprang. The concluding movement is one of Dvořák's most powerful: the anguished dissonances of the first movement are resolved as prelude to an exultant fugal 'Amen'.

Dvořák's *Stabat mater* was rapidly recognised as a masterpiece. Though first performed with very modest forces, it gained a huge following among the choral societies of Victorian England and beyond, doing much to secure the composer an international reputation. When Dvořák himself conducted it at the Royal Albert Hall on his first visit to England in March 1884, he was amazed to be given a choir of 840 voices and an orchestra of 92 strings alone: 'The effect of such an immense body was truly magnificent,' he wrote home to a friend.

Dvořák • Stabat mater
Prom 11 Saturday 27 July, 7.00pm

Lebrecht Music Collection

Schoenberg • Gurrelieder

Chris de Souza highlights the musical and biographical ironies
in the genesis of Schoenberg's most popular score

Gurrelieder may be Arnold Schoenberg's most popular work, but the enormous forces it requires put it beyond the reach of most budgets and concert halls. It is ideal for the Proms and the Royal Albert Hall, though. Fifty woodwind and brass players, four harps and a host of strings create a mind-blowing sound-world, while a massive chorus, five soloists and a speaker tell the story of the Danish king Waldemar's love for the girl Tove. Waldemar's wife has Tove murdered. Waldemar curses God, and is himself cursed to hunt for ever with his vassals every night, though every aspect of nature reminds him of Tove. Part 3 describes the Hunt, and Klaus the Fool's wry comments on the results of Waldemar's curse. The Summer Wind dances and dawn heralds another day.

In 1900, when he began setting Jens Peter Jacobsen's *Songs of Gurre*, Schoenberg was not yet 26. In 1901 he married, and eventually put aside his magnum opus to support his family. He did not return to it for nine years. In the meantime much had changed, his marriage and his music included.

In the course of a stream of masterpieces – *Verklärte Nacht*, *Pelleas und Melisande*, the first two string quartets – Schoenberg had moved from his early voluptuous post-Romanticism and broken the atonal barrier.

He had also experienced a *Gurre*-like crisis of his own. In 1908 his wife had eloped with a painter. When she was finally persuaded to return, the painter had killed himself. What an irony! It was almost as if Schoenberg, like Waldemar's wife, had caused the death of his spouse's lover. This experience inspired his most searingly Expressionistic work, the one-woman drama *Erwartung*.

The final part of *Gurrelieder* is markedly different from, though closely related to, Parts 1 and 2, and works like an epiphany, a wonderful realisation of the earlier music, a truth hard won through heroic effort and tragic experience. As the story works its way from the lovers' heady passion to Klaus the Fool's acerbic comments, the music moves from a rich post-Wagnerian Romanticism to a leaner, reinvigorated sound-world. To sense this in performance is to touch the vital nerve of a man grown wiser, and music history in the making.

Gurrelieder's pantheistic celebration of life carries audiences away. The premiere on 23 February 1913 was Schoenberg's greatest success, greeted with tumultuous applause by a public that had booed almost everything else he had ever written. So both the music and its story are full of ironies. Even as the work reaches its apotheosis in the radiant C major sunrise at the end, one is aware that for Schoenberg, however clearly he saw his own future, not every dawn would be golden.

Schoenberg • Gurrelieder
Prom 13 Sunday 28 July, 7.30pm

BELOW
Arnold Schoenberg, c1905:
a portrait by Richard Gerstl,
the painter who eloped with
the composer's wife, then
killed himself when she went
back to her husband

Rakhmaninov • The Bells

Geoffrey Norris explains how the life-and-death scenario of
Edgar Allan Poe's tintinnabular verses chimed in with the Russian
composer's native fatalism to produce his most personal work

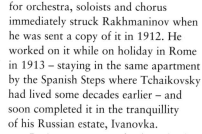

ABOVE
Sergey Rakhmaninov *(top)*
and Edgar Allan Poe: *The Bells*
was the American poet's last
published work and the
Russian composer's favourite
among his own scores

RIGHT
The Tsar Kolokol (or 'King of
Bells') in Moscow's Kremlin
Square: the largest bell in the
world, it was cast in 1733
but cracked in a fire four
years later

Rakhmaninov considered his great choral symphony *The Bells* (*Kolokola*) to be his finest work, and it comes as no surprise that he should have held it in such affection or that he should have written it in the first place. As he once said, 'A love of bells is inherent in every Russian.' For Rakhmaninov, they brought back memories of his childhood in the Novgorod countryside, and conjured up a myriad emotions. The final movement – 'Easter' – in his *Fantaisie-tableaux* for two pianos is a good example of how bell-like textures could colour his own music: small bells, big bells and a smattering of Orthodox chant are all blended together to create an atmosphere of clamorous celebration. Alternatively, in that same piece and in his Pushkin opera *The Miserly Knight*, he could call on a particular chime lurking in the back of his mind to suggest a sense of sorrow. In parts of his setting of the *All-night Vigil* (sometimes known as *Vespers*) he likewise combined the unaccompanied voices in such a way that they have a tolling effect, or resonate with that cumulative clangour redolent of many different peals all ringing at the same time.

Edgar Allan Poe's Gothic poem *The Bells* (1849) might, therefore, have been made for him. Admittedly, it had lost some of its alliteration and assonance in the Russian translation made by the Symbolist poet Konstantin Balmont, but its potential for fuelling four varied movements of a symphony

for orchestra, soloists and chorus immediately struck Rakhmaninov when he was sent a copy of it in 1912. He worked on it while on holiday in Rome in 1913 – staying in the same apartment by the Spanish Steps where Tchaikovsky had lived some decades earlier – and soon completed it in the tranquillity of his Russian estate, Ivanovka.

Poe's verses trace a birth-to-death course, from the silvery sleigh bells of youth, through the mellow bells of maturity and marriage, to the brazen bells of fear and, finally, to the hollow, iron bells of the tomb. For a composer with a naturally fatalistic temperament, such as Rakhmaninov, this last movement struck a particular chord. Nor was there any problem in ending the work with slow music, since there was already a precedent in Tchaikovsky's Sixth Symphony (the 'Pathétique'), and Rakhmaninov responded with a movement that inhabits a deathly stillness until the harmony resolves serenely in the final bars. Here, as elsewhere in this powerful, vivid work, Rakhmaninov, drawing on his command of orchestral colour and expressive melody, establishes the poem's diverse moods in a way that never fails to touch the heart and soul.

Rakhmaninov • The Bells
Prom 27 Friday 9 August, 7.00pm

Mahler • Symphonies Nos. 3 and 8

David Gutman assesses the challenges that confront two of today's leading conductors as they approach Mahler's grandest symphonies

Now that Mahler looms so large in our musical life, it is hard to credit the neglect that followed his premature death. Henry Wood, who had introduced his music to this country with a Proms performance of the First Symphony in 1903, long continued to champion his work in the face of critical disapproval, conducting the British premieres of the Fourth and Seventh Symphonies at the Proms and of the Eighth Symphony at a BBC Queen's Hall concert in 1930. And it was the BBC again that, after a hiatus of some 20 years, came to the rescue with a one-off Royal Albert Hall performance of the Eighth under Jascha Horenstein in March 1959. A curtain-raiser for the Corporation's centenary cycle the following year, it effectively launched our Mahler boom. Yet it only happened at all because there was money left in the budget at the end of the financial year! Even today, such massive scores really need to be heard live, the sheer size of the forces employed (including eight soloists and massed choirs in the case of the so-called 'Symphony of a Thousand') imparting a thrilling sense of occasion.

This year's Proms season includes two of Mahler's grandest symphonies under leading Mahlerians of a younger generation. The Third (1895–6) gives us Mahler the symphonist of nature and love, of spiritual doubts and fears; its six movements run to over 90 minutes. The Eighth (1906) – a rare success for the composer in his own lifetime – is cast in two affirmatory movements: the first sets the Catholic hymn 'Veni Creator Spiritus'; the second is virtually a mini-opera based on the final scene of Goethe's *Faust*. In its closing stages, it reaches for the metaphysical heights as surely as Beethoven's 'Choral' Symphony.

This summer's conductors, Riccardo Chailly and Sir Simon Rattle, share a thoroughly modern desire to re-examine every detail of the scores they perform. Chailly's hallmarks include a fastidious ear for instrumental sonority and a refreshing refusal to over-indulge. Of course, his instrument, the Royal Concertgebouw, boasts a Mahler pedigree dating back to the composer himself, while Chailly seats his musicians as his predecessor Willem Mengelberg once did, exposing the antiphonal effect of divided violins and clarifying solo passages. In the finale of the Seventh, he even uses a unique giant timpani that Mengelberg had built the better to realise Mahler's intentions.

Rattle is also famous for taking every bar seriously, and at white heat. In Mahler's Sixth, he reverses the conventional order of the middle movements. In the Third, he ruffles feathers with his literal reading of the fourth movement's *hinaufziehen* marking, reviving a specific allusion to bird cries on oboe and cor anglais. (Fascinating to see if Chailly goes so far.) For his first-ever account of No. 8, Rattle is working not with forces from Birmingham or Berlin but with the National Youth Orchestra, to which he is no stranger. He recorded Stravinsky's *Rite of Spring* with the NYO when only 23, having himself taken part in an NYO Prom. It will be thrilling to hear their joint response to one of the biggest challenges in musical history.

Mahler • Symphony No. 3	
Prom 52 Wednesday 28 August, 7.30pm	
Mahler • Symphony No. 8	
Prom 30 Sunday 11 August, 7.30pm	

ABOVE
This season's conductors:
Riccardo Chailly and
Sir Simon Rattle

BELOW
Silhouette of Gustav Mahler
conducting, by Otto Böhler

Weber • Euryanthe

John Deathridge argues that the musical merits of Weber's opera more than make up for its absurd plot and nascent German nationalism

ABOVE
Henriette Sontag, the German soprano who created the role of Euryanthe in Vienna in 1823

RIGHT
Carl Maria von Weber

BACKGROUND
Adolar saves Euryanthe from the snake: Act 3 Scene 1 in the 1839 Dresden production

uryanthe is one of the great might-have-beens of opera history. It was commissioned soon after the phenomenal success of Weber's previous opera *Der Freischütz*, first performed in Berlin on 18 June 1821, the sixth anniversary of the Battle of Waterloo. Not only was *Der Freischütz* seen as a nationalist opera that at last could withstand the huge influence on German culture of Napoleonic France, it also helped to set the stage for another work from Weber that could go even further and become a monument to German art on a truly ambitious scale, outdoing even the most high-minded of French operas both scenically and musically.

If *Euryanthe* ultimately failed because of the grand expectations Weber himself had of it, it is still possible today to admire its daring ambition, and to raise the question again of why its marvellous score seems to have been fatally wounded by its libretto. After all, there are many operas (Verdi's *Trovatore*, for example) that easily survive an absurd scenario because of great music. In *Euryanthe*, however, the music Weber had in mind depended from the start for its success on a libretto that would support its drastic local contrasts between good and evil,

and at the same time underpin its grandiose conception of form. In other words, a libretto that would work in the opposite direction to his musical conception by creating a relationship between good and evil that was far from being boldly simple, and a plot which, despite its ungainly dimensions, could stand up to close logical scrutiny.

The libretto of *Euryanthe* fails on both these counts. Weber entrusted it to his friend Helmina von Chezy, who took motifs from a number of medieval sources to elaborate a story of two pairs of lovers – one saintly and crossed by fate, the other fundamentally evil (even to each other) – that revolves around the exculpation of the heroine Euryanthe from all charges of infidelity towards her lover Adolar.

It was Weber, however, who insisted on the work's almost Gothic eccentricities – the ghost of Adolar's sister Emma, for instance, who haunts the overture and who, distraught at the death of her lover Udo, has drunk poison from a ring that eventually falls into the hands of the villainess Eglantine. Weber also insisted that Act 3 open in a rocky mountain gorge where Adolar, having set out to kill his betrothed, is thwarted by an aggressive

snake, which he chases and kills, only then to spare his (former) lover and leave her alone in the wilderness.

Wagner, in writing *Lohengrin*, was heavily influenced by *Euryanthe* and, by his own admission, learnt a good deal from its 'mistakes'. Yet, in a post-Freudian age that has learnt to read into apparently absurd texts from the past something about the repression of powerful instincts and desires, it is certainly possible that the wonderful music Weber poured into *Euryanthe* may still turn out to be part of a truly great work with its own integrity that has been unjustly overshadowed by Wagner. Antipathetic as our age is to the medieval chivalry and early stirrings of German nationalism encoded in *Euryanthe*, this is just the moment to reassess an opera which, despite all the critical scorn poured upon it, may be more meaningful to us than it appears at first sight.

Weber • Euryanthe
Prom 31 Monday 12 August, 7.30pm

Musorgsky • Boris Godunov

David Nice argues that Musorgsky's epic chronicle of Russian history is heard at its most humanly honest and starkly inventive in the composer's original, and shorter, version

It is a very long time indeed since anyone described Musorgsky's *Boris Godunov* as 'the most vulgar and squalid parody of music' – Tchaikovsky's judgement in 1874 – and the need has long since passed to 'improve' upon it, as a well-meaning Rimsky-Korsakov so extensively did in resurrecting it for the opera-going public in the 1890s. We now accept *Boris* in its original form as an uncompromisingly original musical setting of an equally unconventional literary masterpiece.

In 1825 the great Russian poet Alexander Pushkin used Shakespeare's historical dramas as a model for his chronicle of the troubled events of the years 1598 to 1605, following the death of Ivan the Terrible. Sketched in 25 fast-moving scenes, Pushkin's text presents a vortex of political opportunism in which no single figure dominates, although Tsar Boris's alleged guilt as the murderer of the young heir to the throne is here taken as gospel truth and powers several climactic monologues.

Just how timeless Pushkin's message remains was demonstrated in Declan Donnellan's modern-dress production for the Maly Theatre of St Petersburg, which toured to the UK last year, tearing through a chilling slice of Russian history in a gripping two hours. That's about the length, too, of Musorgsky's original, seven-scene opera of 1869. He composed it at a time when he was still especially interested in music drama as 'an artistic reproduction of human speech in all its most subtle forms'. The word-for-word setting he had just attempted of Gogol's comedy *The Marriage* proved too difficult a task, and had to be abandoned. Yet, in choosing his scenes from Pushkin with care, he was indeed faithful to Pushkin's guidelines for 'convincing quality of situations and naturalness of dialogue'. Music could also add the dimension of vivid gesture. A monk painstakingly moving his pen across the page as he records the good and evil he has witnessed; a *yurodivy*, or holy fool, wailing plaintively; a drunken vagabond hiccuping and stammering – these are only the most vivid examples of a flexible style that captures the authentic movement of every character.

In 1872 Musorgsky revised and expanded his opera, partly to suit the Imperial Theatre's wish for a convincing prima donna role. In adding an act set in Poland, where the runaway monk advertising himself as the resurrected Tsarevich woos a power-hungry princess, he was still drawing on Pushkin's original. Yet at the same time, perhaps under the influence of having seen Verdi's *Don Carlos* in St Petersburg, he incorporated more consciously operatic contours into Boris's part. Inevitably, the message of the Tsar's guilt became more melodramatic as a result. Musorgsky's 'second' *Boris* may contain more plums for the singers, but the concentration of the original version – and its total commitment to truthful music-theatre – make it a unique case in the colourful and various history of Russian opera.

Musorgsky • Boris Godunov
Prom 46   Saturday 24 August, 7.30pm

BELOW
Fyodor Chaliapin as Boris Godunov: Alexander Golovin's 1912 portrait of the great Russian bass in his most famous role

BOTTOM LEFT
Ilya Repin's famous portrait of Musorgsky was painted in 1881, just three weeks before the alcoholic composer's death

Gubaidulina • St John Passion

Martin Anderson traces the Orthodox roots of the Russian composer's 'intense, spiritual' tribute to Johann Sebastian Bach

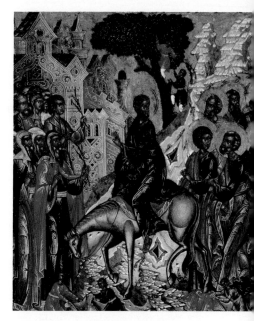

ABOVE
Sofia Gubaidulina: the most Orthodox of 'modernists'

RIGHT
Christ's entry into Jerusalem: an 18th-century Russian icon

After the death of Shostakovich in 1975, a new generation of Soviet composers began to be heard. Chief among them were three 'modernists': Alfred Schnittke, Edison Denisov and Sofia Gubaidulina (born 1931). At least, they seemed modernist at the time, though we can now see them as a natural growth of the Russian tradition, with distant roots in the music of the Orthodox church, in Glinka and the later 19th-century nationalists, Tchaikovsky, Shostakovich and Stravinsky.

Each of the three occupied an individual stylistic niche. Schnittke's German heritage was reflected in his music, with a *Faust Cantata* that reaches back past Goethe into medieval Germany. Denisov was much influenced by French music, an interest reflected in his concern with instrumental colour. And the music of Gubaidulina is a kind of melting-pot, too. Born in Chistopol, Tatarstan, to a Tatar father and a mother of Russian, Polish and Jewish blood, she is, she has said, 'the place where East meets West'.

Her music has always had an intense, spiritual quality to it, with ritual and religious symbolism all-important, even in her instrumental works. So she was a natural choice when the conductor Helmuth Rilling and his

International Bach Academy, Stuttgart, decided to mark the 250th anniversary of Bach's death by asking four very different composers each to write a Passion for 2000 modelled – however distantly – on those of Bach.

The Argentine Osvaldo Golijov's *Pasión según San Marco* is very much a South American affair, pulsing with popular rhythms; the German Wolfgang Rihm's *Deus Passus* sets Paul Celan to put human suffering on a par with that of God; and Tan Dun's *Water Passion after St Matthew* introduces elements of Eastern mysticism. Gubaidulina's *St John Passion* was by far the most ambitious of the four: 90 minutes long, it calls for soprano, alto, tenor and bass soloists, two choruses and a large orchestra, with a substantial percussion section and an organ, amplified piano and synthesiser.

In attempting a Russian Passion, Gubaidulina was presented with a very basic problem: the Orthodox Church does not permit musical instruments – 'no external, technical mediator between man and God – only yourself and a candle in your hand,' as she says. Her solution was to marry the drama of the Western, 'Bachian' tradition with the ritual of Russian religious observance, with the music moving on two different planes,

sometimes simultaneously. Thus the temporal narrative of Christ's passion on Earth is intersected with the Apocalyptic vision of St John, which acts as a commentary from outside of time. The result is both deeply dramatic – often static but crackling with dark energy and elemental tension – and very, very Russian. It, too, has a Hallelujah chorus, whose parentage will be familiar to anyone who knows the Tchaikovsky and Rakhmaninov settings of the Liturgy of St John Chrysostom, and the bells ringing out here are the same as those that ring out over the Coronation Scene in Musorgsky's *Boris Godunov*. Gubaidulina, pushing forward, has also embraced her past.

Gubaidulina • St John Passion
Prom 47 Sunday 25 August (matinee)

71

Sibelius • Kullervo

John Pickard champions the Finnish composer's first flirtation with his country's native myths – a tale of incestuous love that Sibelius himself was surely too quick to disown

Sibelius completed *Kullervo* in April 1892, just days before its triumphant Helsinki premiere. At a stroke, it established the 26-year-old not just as the leading Finnish composer, but as the artistic ambassador for the cause of Finnish nationalism. For Sibelius, this must have presented an uncomfortable dilemma: he was from a Swedish-speaking background and had not previously been associated with the nationalist movement at all.

Kullervo dates from a time of escalating political tension. For centuries, Finland had been the subject of rival territorial claims between Sweden and Russia. In the decades after its annexation by the latter in 1808, the Tsar encouraged the Finns to speak their own language, if only to help check the growth of Swedish influence. But the spread of the Finnish language awakened a new political consciousness among native Finns, and relations with their cosmopolitan Swedish-speaking compatriots became increasingly fraught. Formerly the language of illiterate peasantry, a new Finnish literary culture rapidly developed, focusing growing nationalist awareness through the written word. 1835 saw a decisive step forward with the publication of the *Kalevala*.

This famous collection of Finnish legends is often taken to be an ancient text. In fact, it is a 19th-century anthology of stories transmitted by word of mouth, compiled (and heavily edited) by the scholar Elias Lönnrot. Of course this doesn't diminish the mythological status of the tales, but it does explain the extraordinary impact the *Kalevala* had on 19th-century Finnish society, and why artists of all kinds fell upon it as a rich source of subject-matter.

For Sibelius, it was surely the colour and drama of these legends that provided the initial attraction. A growing sympathy with the cause of Finnish independence was to come later. The *Kalevala* became the basis for most of his tone poems and *Kullervo* was the first and most ambitious. Lasting almost 70 minutes, scored for a large orchestra and incorporating voices in two of its five movements, it tells a story as timeless and universal as anything in Greek tragedy. Kullervo is a tragic figure, doomed from birth: sold into brutal slavery as a child, he exacts a terrible revenge in later life. In a rare moment of happiness, he gains a lover, only to discover – too late – that she is the sister from whom he was parted in infancy. At the close, the incestuous Kullervo's fate is as terrible and pitiful as that of Oedipus.

Sibelius tells this dark tale through music of passionate intensity. Its climactic final pages are among the most electrifying in the whole 19th-century repertoire. Yet Sibelius was dissatisfied with the work, withdrawing the score shortly after the premiere.

Apart from a lone performance of the third movement in 1935, *Kullervo* languished unheard until 1958, a year after Sibelius's death. It has been slow to re-establish itself in the repertoire since then but, thanks to a recent spate of superb performances, is finally being revealed as the blazing masterpiece it is.

Sibelius • Kullervo
Prom 53   Thursday 29 August, 7.30pm

ABOVE
Jean Sibelius in 1894:
a portrait by his friend
Akseli Gallen-Kallela

LEFT
Kullervo's Curse, 1899,
by Akseli Gallen-Kallela

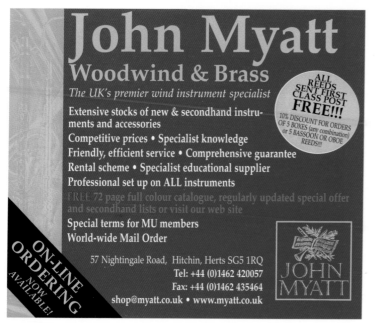
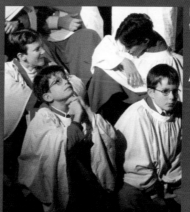

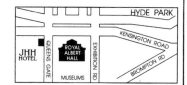

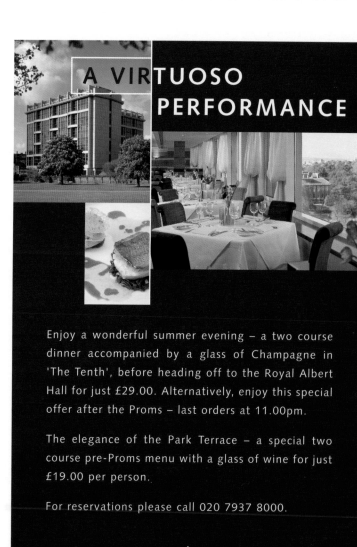

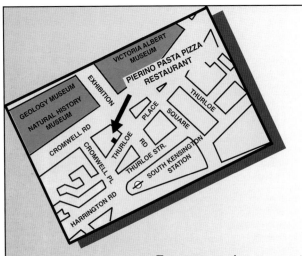
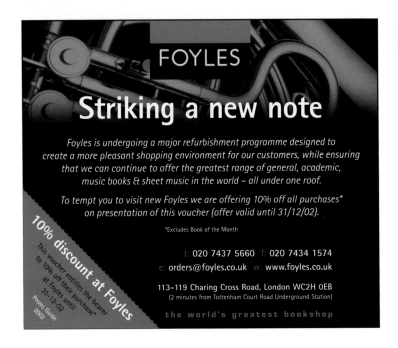

BBC Symphony *Chorus*

Director: Stephen Jackson

'Awesomely excellent' The Times

Join
the BBC Symphony *Chorus*

The BBC Symphony Chorus is one of the finest and most distinctive amateur choirs in the country and performs a wide range of challenging repertoire. The Chorus works closely with the BBC Symphony Orchestra and takes part in the BBC Proms each year as its resident choir, with the First and Last Nights as annual fixtures. The BBC Symphony Chorus regularly performs at the Barbican, tours abroad and has made several CD recordings.

If you love singing and would like to make music at the highest level with great conductors and orchestras, then the BBC Symphony Chorus is for you.

For more information, please contact:

Graham Wood, Administrator, BBC Symphony Chorus,
BBC Maida Vale Studios
Delaware Road, London W9 2LG
Tel: 020 7765 4715 Fax: 020 7286 3251
e-mail: graham.wood@bbc.co.uk

'Flawless' Financial Times

'The BBC Symphony Chorus were magnificent and offered the very finest in choral singing'
Independent on Sunday

'The chorus was vividly dramatic...'
The Guardian

Musical chairs

As batons change hands at the helm of the BBC Philharmonic and BBC Scottish Symphony Orchestras, Lynne Walker talks to the departing maestros and their successors about their memories and expectations of Proms performances past, present and future

Yan Pascal Tortelier

'There's no musician in the world who could resist the thrill and excitement of a packed Albert Hall. I was 15 years old when I made my Proms debut, as the violin soloist in Brahms's Double Concerto with my cellist father, Paul. I was touched then by the warmth of the British public towards me, and to the entire Tortelier family in fact. Now, 40 years on, for my last Prom as the BBC Philharmonic's Principal Conductor, I'm looking forward to a programme of sheer luxury, magic even, beginning with Debussy's mysterious, jewel-like *Nocturnes*. The BBC Philharmonic is sensational in works like Stravinsky's *The Rite of Spring* – I hope it will be an electrifying experience – and Richard Goode's interpretation of Mozart never fails to intrigue and delight.'

'I'm happy to welcome Gianandrea Noseda. After 10 fantastic years for me, it's time for new blood to enter the orchestra.' Yan Pascal Tortelier speaks generously of his Italian successor as Principal Conductor of the BBC Philharmonic, but there is no doubt that, as a special part of Manchester's musical life, Tortelier himself will be missed. His acrobatic feats on the podium, his self-deprecatory sense of humour, his infectious *joie de vivre* and his Gallic charm have all contributed to a unique association over the past decade.

What does Tortelier count among the highlights of his BBC Phil years? Concert performances in Manchester and London of Britten's *Death in Venice*: 'It flatters me above all else to be invited to conduct British music.' And the London premiere (at the Proms) of his own skilfully crafted, virtuoso orchestration of Ravel's Piano Trio, 'exploring the impact of colour within the music'. An investigation into the music of Hindemith in concert and on CD won critical acclaim, and the British premiere of Dutilleux's *The Shadows of Time* – at the 1998 Proms – earned, according to a touching inscription in the conductor's score, 'the gratitude, admiration and affection of Henri Dutilleux'.

'I do not push for French music because I know people will always ask me for it,' says the 55-year-old conductor. Under his baton, the BBC Philharmonic has developed an extensive catalogue of French repertoire on the Chandos label, including works by Lili Boulanger (two of whose psalm settings he introduced at the Proms, in 1999).

'I have found working on French music with the BBC Phil a most rewarding experience, as if it had special appeal for the players. They so easily capture the sensuous world of harmonic colours and sounds, so specific to French repertoire, producing a beautiful and transparent sound.'

But it's not goodbye, only *au revoir*. 'I've enjoyed too strong a relationship with the whole orchestra, and I think also with the audience, to break with them completely.' Others clearly agree and Tortelier takes up a new role as the BBC Philharmonic's Conductor Laureate in the autumn, while pursuing a busy international freelance career. 'It's the most wonderful honour they could pay me. I'm thrilled that the BBC is so keen to see me! Lasting the course and still being

wanted – that is the greatest challenge for any conductor.'

Gianandrea Noseda was, as he puts it, bowled over by the BBC Philharmonic, impressed by the enormously high standard of playing and the quality of individual musicians within the band. He's adamant that a conductor must forge a partnership with an orchestra, become an accomplice – a far cry from the great dictator-conductors of the past. 'I always try to react to an orchestra, to respect its culture and tradition, but here I felt as if I could just be myself and concentrate on making music with these people. I found the BBC Philharmonic totally open and responsive. We trusted each other and I immediately felt at home.'

The 38-year-old maestro, a protégé of Valery Gergiev, at whose invitation Noseda became Principal Guest Conductor of the Kirov Opera, also holds key positions in Rotterdam and Cadaqués in Spain. But he already feels welcome in Manchester, where he declares the Bridgewater Hall 'one of the best I've conducted in' and where his appointment followed a unanimous decision by the players, who admired his Italianate stylishness, his sensitivity and his fresh rehearsal manner.

Three CDs featuring music by an Italian and a Russian – Respighi and Prokofiev – are already scheduled and Noseda is enjoying pinning his own musical colours to the next season, his first as Principal Conductor. 'If I'm honest, I always love the music we're playing now, today. It's the best.'

Gianandrea Noseda

'I attended my first Prom only three years ago and I wished that I could have been standing in the Arena – it looked such fun! I was simply amazed at the informality of the concert, the enthusiasm of the Prommers and the intensity of the whole experience. And these concerts are so famous, all over the world, from America, Japan and Russia to my home in Italy! I never dreamt that I would be lucky enough to be invited to conduct two Proms in my debut season. My first programme with the BBC Philharmonic is irresistible, bursting with zest and vitality. My second concert brings together one of the most atmospheric and painterly scores, in Granados's opera *Goyescas*, with Ravel's brilliant musical comedy *L'Heure espagnole*.'

Andy Farrington

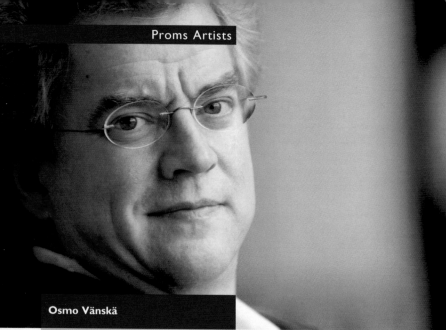

Osmo Vänskä

'One word sums up the Proms for me: festive. My first Prom was in 1995, conducting the BBC Scottish in Sibelius. I remember feeling a bit daunted by the long tradition of the Proms, the enormity of the Albert Hall and the fact that it was my London debut. When I walked onto the stage, I felt such a surge of excitement, it was as if the audience was hungry for us! The Proms audience is one of the most demanding and absolutely the most appreciative. Although this concert is my last as Principal Conductor of the BBC Scottish, I hope to return to this great, great festival. But now that the Albert Hall has air-conditioning, I'll really miss the steamy, hot-house atmosphere of those "sauna" concerts!'

Further north, where another extraordinary musical relationship has blossomed, Osmo Vänskä admits that he will miss his Scottish connection, when he leaves the BBC Scottish Symphony Orchestra this summer. Since he became Chief Conductor in 1996, closing the gap between Lahti – where he continues to be Music Director of the Lahti Symphony Orchestra – and Glasgow, Vänskä has hugely increased the reputation and profile of the BBC SSO. 'We've done great things as a team. They know me. I know them.'

In several memorable 'composer portrait' series he has led the orchestra to a new level, beginning with a distinguished Sibelius cycle. 'I hear people saying that the BBC Scottish is playing noticeably better than a few years ago. I agree, but it is largely down to the musicians' own determination and ability to focus in performance.

My aim has simply been to make every single concert a high point. It's the life behind the notes we're looking for. I want a sound that is not smooth but which has some pepper!'

Beethoven, Nielsen and Rakhmaninov cycles followed the Sibelius, with ground-breaking recordings of most of the Nielsen symphonies, as well as of James MacMillan's triptych *The World's Ransoming*, Cello Concerto and 'Vigil' Symphony. Now, as if the musical world has finally woken up to what Vänskä has to offer, the 49-year-old Finn is juggling invitations, 'running like a horse to fit them all in', and is hard-pushed to find time to play his clarinet or to make chamber music. As for pursuing his passion for motorcycles, that's firmly on the back burner for the time being! He takes over as Music Director at the Minnesota Orchestra next year.

The Israeli-born 25-year-old Ilan Volkov, recently announced as Vänskä's successor, appears unfazed by the responsibility. The youngest conductor ever to lead one of the BBC orchestras, he's cool in his appraisal of the situation: 'It's my first job as Chief Conductor and that is a challenge. But no matter where you are in your life, you have to start somewhere.'

With a brand-new home planned for the BBC SSO at Glasgow's City Hall, a tour of the Far East and China, and his first Prom scheduled for 2003, Volkov joins the BBC's Scottish orchestra at an exciting time. The son of

the respected teacher and pianist in the Israel Piano Trio, Russian émigré Alexander Volkov, Ilan Volkov has wide musical interests. He apparently 'devours' new scores, especially contemporary British music, and enjoys traditional and world sounds, particularly African music.

One of his first projects with the BBC Scottish will feature Schumann's symphonies, while Mahler and Bartók have also been mentioned, as well as the possibility of exploring Baroque repertoire. He felt an instant affinity with the musicians, he says: 'You never know how you will feel with an orchestra but here there was an understanding; everybody just wanted to make great music.'

BBC Philharmonic
Gianandrea Noseda conducts his first Proms as Principal Conductor Proms 3 and 18

Yan Pascal Tortelier conducts his last Prom as Principal Conductor Prom 62

BBC Scottish Symphony Orchestra
Osmo Vänskä conducts his last Prom as Chief Conductor Prom 14

BELOW
Ilan Volkov, the BBC Scottish Symphony Orchestra's 25-year-old Chief Conductor Designate

BBC Philharmonic

Founded in 1934 as the BBC Northern Orchestra and renamed the BBC Northern Symphony Orchestra in 1967, the BBC's Manchester-based band survived repeated threats of disbandment over the years until a musicians' strike in 1980 finally secured its future as the 90-strong BBC Philharmonic. It made its Proms debut in 1961 under George Hurst, its then Principal Conductor, with a programme featuring the premiere of Anthony Milner's *Divertimento* for strings.

Also conducting the BBC Philharmonic are:

Vassily Sinaisky Prom 19
The orchestra's Principal Guest Conductor returns with a mainly Russian programme of Shostakovich, Rakhmaninov and Shchedrin.

Rumon Gamba Prom 65 and CBBC Prom in the Park
Winner of the 1998 BBC Young Musicians Conductors' Workshop, the orchestra's Assistant Conductor presides over both this summer's family-friendly Proms.

BBC Scottish Symphony Orchestra

Founded in 1935 as the BBC Scottish Orchestra, with a remit to play mainly light music, the orchestra's expansion into more serious repertoire was recognised when it was renamed the BBC Scottish Symphony Orchestra in 1967. It made its Proms debut in 1962, under its then Chief Conductor Norman Del Mar, with a programme that included the premiere of Scottish composer Thea Musgrave's *The Phoenix and the Turtle*.

Also conducting the BBC SSO are:

Ion Marin Prom 25
A Romanian-born Swiss resident with Austrian citizenship, Marin makes his Proms debut with an equally multinational mix of Shostakovich, Strauss and Walton.

Martyn Brabbins Prom 27
Associate Principal Conductor of the BBC SSO since 1994, the Leningrad-trained Martyn Brabbins conducts music by the Russians Rakhmaninov and Rimsky-Korsakov and the Spaniard Manuel de Falla.

BBC Symphony Orchestra

Founded in 1930, the BBC Symphony Orchestra played for every Prom throughout its first decade. Nowadays, with more time devoted to preparation and rehearsal, the BBC SO is still the linchpin of the season, giving more concerts than any other orchestra, but now shares the bill with its fellow BBC orchestras and with visiting groups from both home and abroad. This season, in addition to five concerts under its Chief Conductor, Leonard Slatkin, it will be playing a further eight concerts under seven other conductors.

Leonard Slatkin Proms 1, 5, 39, 69, 73

The BBC SO's Los Angeles-born Chief Conductor launches into his second Proms season with a new piece he premiered with his Washington orchestra last year, then conducts the first of this year's four BBC Proms commissions (see page 45). After pursuing our Spanish theme through a Russian reworking of *Carmen* and gypsy pieces by Ravel and Sarasate, he joins his compatriot André Watts in Rakhmaninov's most popular piano concerto, before finally bringing his personal touch to bear on the traditional format of the Last Night.

Donald Runnicles Prom 13

Music Director of the San Francisco Opera since 1992, Edinburgh-born Donald Runnicles made his

Proms debut in 2000 conducting the BBC SO in Robin Holloway's new Symphony and the last act of Wagner's *Die Walküre*. He returns for Schoenberg's suitably post-Wagnerian *Gurrelieder*.

Sir Andrew Davis Prom 17, 22

Andrew Davis stepped down after 11 years as Chief Conductor of the BBC SO at the end of the 2000 Proms season, only to be reborn as the orchestra's first ever Conductor Laureate. Currently Music Director of the Lyric Opera of Chicago, he returns to conduct two of the season's major BBC commissions – the new central panel of Mark-Anthony Turnage's ongoing orchestral triptych and *Visions and Journeys*, Anthony Payne's first big new score since his completion of Elgar's Third Symphony, which Davis so memorably premiered.

Enrique Diemecke Prom 26

Music Director of the Orquesta Sinfónica Nacional de México since 1990, this Mexican-born son of German musicians makes his Proms debut in a masterpiece by Mexico's most famous composer.

Pierre Boulez Prom 33

Figurehead of the post-war avant-garde, this former Chief Conductor of the BBC SO returns to the Proms to conduct his old orchestra in key 20th-century works by Stravinsky, Varèse and himself.

Thomas Adès Prom 53

Having already made his Proms debut directing a piece of his own from the piano in 1998, the multi-talented young composer-conductor-

ABOVE
A group photograph of the BBC Symphony Orchestra and Adrian Boult, its first Chief Conductor, taken before their inaugural concert at the Queen's Hall on 22 October 1930

Leonard Slatkin   Donald Runnicles   Sir Andrew Davis   Enrique Diemecke   Pierre Boulez   Thomas Adès   Ingo Metzmacher

performer now makes his full conducting debut at the Proms in a personal mix of music by Berlioz, Sibelius and himself.

Ingo Metzmacher Prom 57

The General Music Director of the City of Hamburg since 1997, Metzmacher made his Proms debut in 2000 conducting the UK premiere of Henze's Ninth Symphony, the world premiere of which he had conducted in Berlin. He returns with an idiosyncratic pairing of Ives and Mahler.

Christoph Eschenbach Prom 63

Currently Music Director in Hamburg, Paris and Philadelphia, this former international concert pianist marks his BBC SO conducting debut with the UK premiere of a new work composed especially for his Paris orchestra and premiered by them in New York last January (see page 43).

BBC National Orchestra of Wales

Evolving from an ad hoc group of players known as the Cardiff Studio Orchestra, the BBC Welsh Orchestra was founded, like its Scottish counterpart, in 1935. Renamed the BBC Welsh Symphony Orchestra in 1974 and the BBC National Orchestra of Wales in 1993, it now makes its performing home at St David's Hall, Cardiff. It made its Proms debut in 1971 with a programme of Haydn, Mozart, Brahms and Stravinsky, conducted by Irwin Hoffman.

Richard Hickox Proms 11, 60

The BBC NOW's Principal Conductor since September 2000 and a long-term champion of British music, Hickox conducts two Proms pairing works by centenary composer William Walton with classics by Dvořák and Brahms.

Tadaaki Otaka Prom 16

Conductor Laureate of both the BBC NOW and the Tokyo Philharmonic, Otaka made his Proms debut in 1988 and returns this year for a programme of French and Polish classics.

Joseph Swensen Prom 35

Principal Guest Conductor of both the BBC NOW and the Lahti Symphony Orchestra, Swensen was born in New York to parents of Norwegian and Japanese descent and now lives in Copenhagen. He made his Proms debut with the Scottish Chamber Orchestra, of which he is Principal Conductor, in 1999 and returns this year with a German-Scandinavian mix of Nielsen, Schumann and Sibelius.

BBC Concert Orchestra

Founded in 1952, the BBC Concert Orchestra made its Proms debut five years later under Vilem Tausky. Now based at the Hippodrome, Golders Green, where it has hosted Radio 2's *Friday Night Is Music Night* for 45 years, it launched its 50th anniversary season with a 14-state tour of the USA.

Barry Wordsworth Prom 41

Having conducted the BBC Concert Orchestra at every Proms season since becoming its Principal Conductor in 1989, Barry Wordsworth returns for a Latin-American programme featuring star Mexican tenor Ramón Vargas.

David Charles Abell Prom 37

A former pupil of Leonard Bernstein, Abell is equally at home in grand opera and Broadway musicals and makes his Proms debut conducting our centenary tribute to Richard Rodgers.

Miguel Harth-Bedoya Prom 64

Born in Lima, Peru, the 33-year-old Associate Conductor of the Los Angeles Philharmonic makes his Proms debut with a Latin-American mix of Ginastera, Piazzolla and more.

See also 'Musical chairs', pages 80–83

Christoph Eschenbach   Richard Hickox   Tadaaki Otaka   Joseph Swensen   David Charles Abell   Barry Wordsworth   Miguel Harth-Bedoya

The first Last Night after the one before

Louise Downes celebrates the latest developments in the long-running Proms tradition of change and renewal

The date alone should be sufficient explanation: last year's Last Night fell on 15 September. In the light of that week's events, it was inconceivable that the advertised concert – with its second half of American showpieces leading into the traditional sequence of *Pomp and Circumstance*, *British Sea-Songs*, *Rule, Britannia!* and *Jerusalem* – could have gone ahead as planned. Instead, the great choral finale from Beethoven's Ninth Symphony sounded the climax to a rapidly revised programme designed to display music's unique ability to affirm our shared humanity. *Jerusalem* was then sung to bring the concert to a close.

A big break with tradition then. Or was it? In fact, the so-called 'traditional' Last Night foursome of Elgar-Wood-Arne-Parry only really solidified in 1987. Before then, Last Night audiences might well have heard most of these works but rarely all four together, and never in an unbroken sequence. And indeed, when it comes to the Last Night, as with the Proms in general, the tradition has always been one of change and innovation within a strong framework of continuity.

Thus the 'tradition' of Friday First Nights only began in 1968, when the season opened a day early to make room for a memorial concert to Malcolm Sargent, who had died the year before.

Just so, Wood's famous *Fantasia on British Sea-Songs* was originally devised for a special Nelson Centenary matinee concert on Trafalgar Day in 1905, and – contrary to Wood's own recollections in *My Life of Music* (1938) – didn't make it into the Last Night until 1908 and only became a regular fixture in the 1920s.

Equally, the big tune in Elgar's first *Pomp and Circumstance* march – a work given its London premiere by Wood in 1901 – only acquired its familiar words a year later, when it was recycled as the 'Land of Hope and Glory' section of the *Coronation Ode* that Elgar wrote for Edward VII. And, though Elgar's march went on to become a popular Proms item, it only appeared spasmodically at Last Nights until as recently as 1950.

Ironically, those two other staples of the 'traditional' Last Night line-up – Sargent's version of *Rule, Britannia!* and Parry's *Jerusalem* – actually made their joint Last Night debut in 1953 in place of Wood's *Sea-Songs*, which the BBC's then Head of Music, Maurice Johnstone, had decided to drop, feeling that their 'jingoism' was 'out of date' and that their element of audience participation,

Last Night Ballot

Exclusive to readers of the Proms Guide

One hundred best seats (priced £75.00) for the Last Night of the Proms at the Royal Albert Hall will be allocated by ballot to readers of the *BBC Proms 2002 Guide*. The 'Six Concert Rule' does not apply, and no other ticket purchases are necessary. Only one application (for a maximum of two tickets) may be made per household.

If you would like to apply for tickets by ballot, please complete the official Ballot Form on the back of this slip (photocopies are not acceptable) and send it by post only – to arrive no later than Friday 19 July – to:

**BBC Proms Ballot,
Box Office,
Royal Albert Hall,
London SW7 2AP**

Note that the Proms Ballot application is completely separate from other Proms booking procedures. Envelopes should be clearly marked 'BBC PROMS BALLOT' and should contain only the official Ballot Form, together with your cheque or card details. If sending a cheque, please also enclose an SAE so that it can be returned to you if your application is unsuccessful. Successful applicants will be notified by post within two weeks of the ballot, which takes place on Friday 2 August.

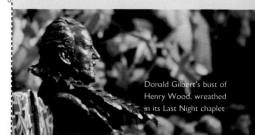

Donald Gilbert's bust of Henry Wood, wreathed in its Last Night chaplet

Last Night Ballot Form

Title   Initial

Surname

Address

Postcode

Country

Daytime tel.

Please tick the appropriate boxes

☐ I wish to apply for one ticket (£75.00)

☐ I wish to apply for two tickets (£150.00)

☐ I enclose a cheque made payable to
'Royal Albert Hall' and an SAE.
(Cheques will be returned to unsuccessful
applicants within two weeks of the ballot.)

☐ Please debit my Access/Visa/Amex/
Mastercard/Switch*

☐☐☐☐☐☐☐☐☐☐☐☐☐☐☐☐

Expiry Date   Issue No.*

☐☐☐☐   ☐☐

Signature

which Wood himself always encouraged, had got out of hand. In the event, mass protests ensured that the *Sea-Songs* were included after all, as an encore, and they were back on the official Last Night agenda the following year, though from then until Sargent's death his solo vocal version of *Rule, Britannia!* invariably displaced Wood's original arrangement for organ and orchestra, with its open invitation to community singing.

It was to offer Last Night audiences an even bigger opportunity for self-expression that both Wood and Sargent were dropped for three years running in the early 1970s in order to make way for a series of specially commissioned new audience-participation pieces by Malcolm Arnold, Malcolm Williamson and Gordon Crosse. Last Night premieres have since become a new tradition: Harrison Birtwistle's *Panic* made a memorable debut in 1995, since when novelties of one kind or another in the first part of the concert have continued to feature at every Last Night.

So what does this year's Last Night have to offer? As usual, there's a tying together of some of the strands of the season, with Walton's 1953 coronation march *Orb and Sceptre* linking his centenary to the Queen's Golden Jubilee. The royal theme is also echoed in a new set of Purcell variations, inspired by a Coronation Year model, and in Hubert Parry's *I Was Glad*, composed for the coronation of Edward VII, as well as in Walton's film music for *Henry V* (in another of Malcolm Sargent's arrangements). Plus there's a great popular classic to end Part 1:

Grieg's Piano Concerto, played by its foremost interpreter, who just happens to be a Norwegian like its composer.

Pomp and Circumstance returns to its old spot at the start of Part 2. *Jerusalem* is there too and the National Anthem (in Britten's arrangement). In between, there's a centenary nod at Richard Rodgers, with a set of his show tunes sung by a young Broadway star who made a memorable Proms debut in Bernstein's conga-crazy *Wonderful Town* a few years back. And also Sullivan's overture to *The Yeomen of the Guard* – a work Wood knew well, having been the rehearsal pianist for its 1888 premiere – to provide a bridge between Britain's musical theatre and America's.

And finally there's Leonard Slatkin, the BBC Symphony Orchestra's US-born Chief Conductor, who, having made such a powerful impression channelling the emotions at last year's Last Night, will this year be able to do what he'd promised to do then – to bring his own personal touch to bear on this most British of musical institutions by playing the master of ceremonies, perhaps, rather more than the speech-maker.

So the answer to the question 'What does this year's Last Night have to offer?' is really 'Tradition', but a tradition refreshed for another year.

ABOVE
Malcolm Sargent, who did so much to shape the character of the Last Night of the Proms following his appointment as Chief Conductor of the BBC Symphony Orchestra in 1950

The Last Night of the Proms
Prom 73 Saturday 14 September
For full listing, see page 108
For special booking arrangements,
see page 119
For BBC Proms in the Park,
see pages 109 and 129

How to book

Your copy of the *BBC Proms 2002 Guide* contains a tear-out form for Priority Booking. For your best chance of securing the tickets you want, fill it in and post or fax it to arrive at the Royal Albert Hall Box Office by Monday 20 May. This is the day on which the Box Office will begin issuing tickets. Please note that Express bookings will be handled first (see *page 121 for details*).

You can also use our new Online Ticket Request system for Priority Booking. Online requests will be processed at the same time as postal and fax bookings, starting on Monday 20 May. Visit the BBC Proms website for details: www.bbc.co.uk/proms

Note that until general booking opens on Monday 17 June, only bookings made on the official Booking Form or via the Online Ticket Request system will be accepted.

The Last Night of the Proms

Because of the high demand for tickets, special booking arrangements apply. See page 119

Special Offers

For Special Offers, see pages 112–113.
Fold out the flap on page 121 for a handy reminder of standard prices and special offers while reading through the listings.

Priority Booking
By post, fax and online – opens Monday 20 May

Use the Booking Form or visit www.bbc.co.uk/proms

To take advantage of the Priority Booking period – and enjoy your best chance of securing the seats you want – use the official tear-out Booking Form (facing page 122) or visit the Proms website. Note that all postal, fax and online bookings received before 20 May will be treated as if they had arrived on that date.

Postal address: BBC Proms, Box Office, Royal Albert Hall, London SW7 2AP

Fax number: 020 7581 9311
Online booking: www.bbc.co.uk/proms

General Booking
In person, by phone or online – opens Monday 17 June

The Box Office is located at Door 12 of the Royal Albert Hall and is open 9.00am–9.00pm daily. Note that no booking fee applies to tickets bought in person at the Hall.

Telephone number: 020 7589 8212
Online booking: www.bbc.co.uk/proms

Last Night Ballot

Exclusive to readers of the *BBC Proms 2002 Guide*

Your chance to enter this year's Last Night Ballot and apply for tickets to the Last Night. See page 87.

Promming on the Day

Don't book, just turn up

Up to 1,400 standing places are available at each Proms concert. Season Tickets and Weekend Passes can be booked in advance: see page 118. But over 500 Arena and Gallery tickets are always on sale at the door, so you can just turn up on the night.

Special Offers

Proms Explorers
Choose three or four concerts from either the Spanish Explorer or the Choral Explorer selection and save 10%. Choose five or more concerts and save 15% and enjoy a free Late Night Prom as well.

Weekend Promming Pass
Beat the queues and save money too.

Same Day Savers
Book for two concerts on the same day and save £2.00.

Group Bookings
Book 10 or more tickets for any Prom in the A or B price bands (Centre/Side Stalls and Front/Rear Circle only) and save 10%.

Under-16s
Save 50% on seats for marked concerts.

For full details of all Special Offers, see pages 112–113

Pre-Prom Talk venues
RAH • Royal Albert Hall (Auditorium)
RCM • Royal College of Music

All concert details were correct at the time of going to press. The BBC reserves the right to alter artist or programme details as necessary

PROM 1

Friday 19 July
7.30pm – c9.40pm
Price Code **C**

Chabrier
España   6'

Roberto Sierra
Fandangos   12'
UK premiere

Lalo
Symphonie espagnole   33'

interval

Walton
Belshazzar's Feast   35'

Maxim Vengerov *violin*
Willard W. White *bass-baritone*

Choral Arts Society of Washington
BBC Symphony Chorus
BBC Symphony Orchestra
Leonard Slatkin *conductor*

Maxim Vengerov

Willard W. White

This year's Proms season opens with a Spanish fiesta and a pagan feast. Walton's dionysiac cantata vividly depicts the fall of Babylon and kicks off our celebration of the composer's centenary (see pages 52–54) and our survey of Old Testament tales (see pages 28–31). Spain, another of this year's themes, is evoked in a pair of colourful works by French composers (see pages 17–21) – Chabrier's vivid showpiece, and Lalo's most enduringly popular work with the charismatic young violinist Maxim Vengerov – plus Puerto Rican composer Roberto Sierra's gloss on Soler's 18th-century fandango (see page 45). The BBC Symphony Orchestra and Chorus are joined by guests from Washington DC, Chief Conductor Leonard Slatkin's other musical home.

This concert will be broadcast on BBC2

💬 **6.00pm Poetry Prom**
See page 133

PROM 2

Saturday 20 July
7.30pm – c9.45pm
Price Code **B**

Haydn
The Creation *(sung in German)*   109'

Christiane Oelze *soprano*
Paul Groves *tenor*
John Relyea *bass*

Choir of the Enlightenment
Orchestra of the Age of Enlightenment
Sir Charles Mackerras *conductor*

Retracing our Old Testament theme to its beginning, Haydn's life-enhancing account of the story of Genesis – a landmark of the Enlightenment – is presented by one of the leading period-instrument groups under the baton of Sir Charles Mackerras, who was among the first conductors to embrace the possibilities of historical performance.

There will be one interval

This concert will be broadcast on BBC4

💬 **6.00pm Pre-Prom Talk** (RAH)
Nicholas Kenyon and David Wyn Jones on *The Creation*

PROM 3
Sunday 21 July
7.00pm – c9.00pm
Price Code A

The Nation's Favourite Prom

Bernstein
Candide – Overture   5'

Gershwin
Songs with orchestra   c15'
Rhapsody in Blue   16'

interval

Bizet
Carmen – Habanera; Seguidilla   7'

Saint-Saëns
Samson and Delilah – Bacchanale;
'Mon coeur s'ouvre à ta voix'   14'

Ravel
Boléro   16'

Denyce Graves *mezzo-soprano*
Jean-Yves Thibaudet *piano*

BBC Philharmonic
Gianandrea Noseda *conductor*

The BBC Philharmonic's new Principal
Conductor (see pages 80–83) makes
his Proms debut in a concert of
popular classics. A well-loved Proms
soloist plays Gershwin's jazz rhapsody
and an opera star makes her Proms
debut in popular songs and arias picking
up on our Hispanic and Biblical themes.

This concert will be broadcast on BBC1

💬 **5.00pm BBC Proms Lecture**
'Libeskind Variations'. *See page 132*

PROM 4
Monday 22 July
7.30pm – c9.30pm
Price Code A

Berlioz
Overture 'Roman Carnival'   8'

Bruch
Violin Concerto No. 1   24'

interval

Messiaen
L'ascension   24'

Ravel
La valse   12'

Kyung-Wha Chung *violin*

**Orchestre Philharmonique
de Radio France**
Myung-Whun Chung *conductor*

Kyung-Wha
Chung

Myung-Whun Chung,
who enjoys a special
association with the music
of Messiaen, is a leading
conductor of opera and
orchestras in Paris. He
brings to the Proms the orchestra of
which he is now Principal Conductor.
His sister, in a rare London appearance,
performs a favourite violin concerto.

This concert will be broadcast on BBC4

🎵 **1.00pm Proms Chamber Music**
See pages 110–111

PROM 5
Tuesday 23 July
7.00pm – c9.10pm
Price Code A

Elgar
In the South (Alassio)   20'

David Sawer
Piano Concerto   c18'
BBC commission: world premiere

interval

Ravel
Shéhérazade   15'

Stravinsky
The Firebird (excerpts from original
ballet chosen by Leonard Slatkin)   30'

Frederica von Stade *mezzo-soprano*
Rolf Hind *piano*

BBC Symphony Orchestra
Leonard Slatkin *conductor*

Frederica
von Stade

Prevented from appearing
at last year's Last Night
by the events of 11
September, the famous
American singer Frederica
von Stade makes her
belated Proms debut. David Sawer's
Piano Concerto is the first of this year's
BBC commissions (see page 45) and
follows the success of his opera *From
Morning to Midnight* at ENO last year.

This concert will be broadcast on BBC4

🎵 **5.30pm Composer Portrait**
David Sawer. *See page 134*

PROM 6
Tuesday 23 July
10.00pm – c11.40pm
Price Code E

Handel
Israel in Egypt   94'

Katharine Fuge, Gillian Keith
sopranos
**Daniel Taylor, William Towers,
Richard Wyn-Roberts** *altos*
**Andrew Busher, Andrew
Mackenzie-Wicks** *tenors*
Michael Bundy, Daniel Jordan *basses*

Monteverdi Choir
Monteverdi Orchestra
Sir John Eliot Gardiner *conductor*

Handel's choral masterpiece, setting
the story of the exile of the Israelites,
contains some of his most vivid
pictorial writing, including the famous
'plague' choruses (see pages 28–31).
Sir John Eliot Gardiner and his
Monteverdi Choir and Orchestra
continue their long and triumphant
association with the Proms.

There will be no interval

PROM 7

Wednesday 24 July
7.30pm – c9.55pm
Price Code **A**

Gerhard
Concerto for Orchestra   22'

Mendelssohn
Violin Concerto in E minor   27'

interval

Xavier Montsalvatge
Canciones negras   15'

Falla
The Three-Cornered Hat   37'

Viktoria Mullova *violin*
Jennifer Larmore *mezzo-soprano*

Orquestra Simfónica de Barcelona
Lawrence Foster *conductor*

In this Spanish year at the Proms, the Orquestra Simfonica de Barcelona appears here for the first time, bringing Falla's colourful ballet (see page 8) and Mendelssohn's well-loved concerto. Proms debut artist Jennifer Larmore celebrates the 90th birthday of Spanish composer Xavier Montsalvatge, and the concert opens with a BBC commission of the 1960s from a Catalan composer who made his home in this country (see page 9).

This concert will be broadcast on BBC4

💬 **6.00pm Pre-Prom Talk** (RAH)
Michael Oliver on the music of Spain

PROM 8

Thursday 25 July
7.00pm – c9.00pm
Price Code **A**

Hans Werner Henze
Fandango (1995 version)   12'

Beethoven
Piano Concerto No. 3 in C minor   36'

interval

Vaughan Williams
Symphony No. 4 in F minor   32'

Paul Lewis *piano*

Bournemouth Symphony
Orchestra
Paul Daniel *conductor*

Paul Lewis

The award-winning team of Paul Daniel and the Bournemouth Symphony Orchestra perform a quirky fandango by Hans Werner Henze and Vaughan Williams's powerful inter-war symphony. Paul Lewis, who had been due to appear at last year's Last Night, plays Beethoven's fate-tinged concerto.

This concert will be broadcast on BBC4

PROM 9

Thursday 25 July
10.00pm – c11.30pm
Price Code **E**

The Oriana Collection

Bennet
All Creatures Now Are Merry Minded

Weelkes
As Vesta was from Latmos Hill Descending

Johnson
Come, Blessed Bird

and other selections from 'The Triumphs of Oriana' interspersed with new works (to specially commissioned poems) by:

Joe Duddell (Gracie Nichols)
Howard Goodall (U. A. Fanthorpe)
John Harle (Ian Sinclair)
John McCabe (Jo Shapcott)
Dominic Muldowney (Simon Armitage)
Jocelyn Pook (Andrew Motion)
Joby Talbot (Kathleen Jamie)
BBC/King'singers commission:
world premiere

King'singers

The Oriana Collection is a set of modern madrigals by leading composers and poets specially commissioned to celebrate the Queen's Golden Jubilee. The 1601 madrigal collection *The Triumphs of Oriana* was written in honour of Queen Elizabeth I (see page 39).

There will be no interval

This concert will be broadcast on BBC4

PROM 10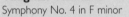

Friday 26 July
7.30pm – c9.40pm
Price Code **A**

Oliver Knussen
Where the Wild Things Are   40'

interval

Oliver Knussen
Higglety, Pigglety, Pop!   62'

Rosemary Hardy *soprano*
Valdine Anderson *soprano*
Mary King *mezzo-soprano*
Christopher Gillett *tenor*
Quentin Hayes *baritone*
David Wilson-Johnson *bass-baritone*
Stephen Richardson *bass*

London Sinfonietta
Oliver Knussen *conductor*

The 50th birthday of the London Sinfonietta's Music Director is celebrated with concert performances of his two enchanting Glyndebourne-commissioned fantasy operas based on Maurice Sendak's classic tales (see pages 56–57). Suitable for children of all ages!

This concert will be broadcast on BBC4

🎵 **6.00pm Proms Extra**
A Wild Rumpus. See page 131

PROM 11

Saturday 27 July
7.00pm – c8.45pm
Price Code **A**

NOTE TIME

Walton, arr. Palmer
Christopher Columbus – Suite   11'

Dvořák
Stabat mater   81'

Susan Chilcott *soprano*
Catherine Wyn-Rogers
mezzo-soprano
Jorma Silvasti *tenor*
John Tomlinson *bass*

BBC National Chorus of Wales
London Symphony Chorus
BBC National Orchestra of Wales
Richard Hickox *conductor*

A suite drawn from centenary composer
William Walton's music for a BBC radio
play by Louis MacNeice prefaces music
by a composer who followed in
Columbus's footsteps to the New
World. The BBC National Orchestra
of Wales's performance of the *Stabat
mater* is the culmination of the
orchestra's exploration of Dvořák's
music under its Principal Conductor,
Richard Hickox (see page 65).

There will be no interval

This concert will be broadcast on BBC4

💬 **5.30pm Pre-Prom Talk** (RCM)
Richard Hickox in conversation with
Stephanie Hughes

PROM 12

Saturday 27 July
10.00pm – c11.30pm
Price Code **E**

LATE NIGHT

United in Swing

Lincoln Center Jazz Orchestra
Wynton Marsalis *trumpet/director*

Wynton Marsalis

Making a welcome return
after his previous Proms
visit with his septet, the
charismatic American
trumpet virtuoso,
educationalist and musical
dynamo Wynton Marsalis returns with
the larger forces of his Lincoln Center
Jazz Orchestra for a Late Night
programme celebrating the irresistible
rhythms and roof-lifting riffs of the
Golden Age of Swing – a time when
the ballrooms of the world were
ruled by the classic big-band sounds
of Count Basie, Chick Webb,
Jimmie Lunceford and Duke Ellington.

There will be no interval

This concert will be broadcast on BBC1

PROM 13

Sunday 28 July
7.30pm – c9.25pm
Price Code **A**

Schoenberg
Gurrelieder   106'

Christine Brewer *Tove*
Ben Heppner *Waldemar*
Petra Lang *Wood-Dove*
Philip Langridge *Klaus*
Peter Sidhom *Peasant*
Ernst Haefliger *Speaker*

Geoffrey Mitchell Choir
BBC Symphony Chorus
Philharmonia Chorus
BBC Symphony Orchestra
Donald Runnicles *conductor*

Following his success with Wagner
two years ago, Donald Runnicles
returns with Schoenberg's awe-inspiring
early masterpiece, in which the musical
languages of two centuries mingle (see
page 66). Canadian heldentenor Ben
Heppner makes his Proms debut as
Waldemar, the self-cursed king, and
we welcome the Proms return – after
more than three decades – of the
octogenarian Swiss tenor Ernst
Haefliger as the Speaker.

There will be no interval

This concert will be broadcast on BBC4

💬 **6.00pm Pre-Prom Talk** (RAH)
John Deathridge on *Gurrelieder*

PROM 14

Monday 29 July
7.30pm – c9.30pm
Price Code **A**

Sibelius
Tapiola   18'

Mozart
Piano Concerto No. 23 in A major,
K488   26'

interval

Nielsen
Symphony No. 4,
'The Inextinguishable'   36'

Stephen Hough *piano*

BBC Scottish Symphony Orchestra
Osmo Vänskä *conductor*

In his last appearance after a
triumphant period as Chief Conductor
of the BBC Scottish Symphony
Orchestra, Osmo Vänskä presents the
last orchestral work by his compatriot
Sibelius, and the 'Inextinguishable'
Symphony of Nielsen, whose
symphonies he has been recording
with the orchestra. They are joined by
Stephen Hough for one of the most
lyrical of Mozart's piano concertos.

This concert will be broadcast on BBC4

♪ **1.00pm Proms Chamber Music**
See pages 110–111

PROM 15 ⓖ

Tuesday 30 July
7.30pm – c9.50pm
Price Code **A**

Per Nørgård
Symphony No. 6, 'At the End
of the Day'   31'
UK premiere

Nielsen
Violin Concerto   36'

interval

Brahms
Symphony No. 1 in C minor   45'

Nikolaj Znaider *violin*

**Danish National Symphony
Orchestra**
Thomas Dausgaard *conductor*

Nikolaj
Znaider

Denmark's fine
broadcasting orchestra and
its charismatic conductor
bring to the Proms their
compatriot Per Nørgård's
quirky millennium
symphony (*see page 44*), and fellow
Dane Nikolaj Znaider makes his Proms
debut with Nielsen's Violin Concerto in
only its second ever Proms performance.
Brahms's First Symphony, which looks
back to the music of Beethoven and
Bach, completes the bill.

This concert will be broadcast on BBC4

💬 **6.00pm Pre-Prom Talk** (RAH)
Per Nørgård in conversation with
Stephen Johnson

PROM 16 ⒠ⓖ

Wednesday 31 July
7.00pm – c9.00pm
Price Code **A**

NOTE
TIME

Ravel
Rapsodie espagnole   15'

Szymanowski
Violin Concerto No. 1   24'

interval

Debussy
Première rapsodie   8'

Lutoslawski
Concerto for Orchestra   29'

Kyoko Takezawa *violin*
Ronald van Spaendonck *clarinet*

BBC National Orchestra of Wales
Tadaaki Otaka *conductor*

The Spanish theme of this year's Proms
continues with Ravel's exotic French
view of the south (*see pages 17–21*).
Ronald van Spaendonck is a Radio 3
New Generation Artist, and Kyoko
Takezawa revives Szymanowski's
rarely-heard First Violin Concerto.
The exuberant post-war classic by
fellow Pole Lutoslawski completes this
concert by the BBC NOW under its
Conductor Laureate.

This concert will be broadcast on BBC4

PROM 17 ⓖ

Thursday 1 August
7.30pm – c9.40pm
Price Code **A**

Debussy
Prélude à L'après-midi d'un faune   10'

Mark-Anthony Turnage
Uninterrupted Sorrow   c15'
BBC commission: world premiere

Ravel
Piano Concerto for the Left Hand   19'

interval

Vaughan Williams
Job: A Masque for Dancing   43'

Louis Lortie *piano*

BBC Symphony Orchestra
Sir Andrew Davis *conductor*

The BBC SO's Conductor Laureate is
welcomed back to the Proms with a
pairing of Debussy and Ravel, alongside
a new work by Mark-Anthony Turnage,
which will form the centrepiece
of a triptych for the BBC Symphony
Orchestra (*see page 45*). The season's
Old Testament theme continues with a
rare revival of Vaughan Williams's
masque (*see pages 28–31*).

This concert will be broadcast on BBC4

💬 **6.00pm Pre-Prom Talk** (RAH)
Mark-Anthony Turnage in conversation
with Barrie Gavin

PROM 18 ⒠ⓦ ⓖ

Friday 2 August
7.30pm – c9.45pm
Price Code **A**

Granados
Goyescas (*sung in Spanish*)   60'

Angela Marambio *Rosario*
Sarah Connolly *Pepa*
Marius Brenciu *Fernando*
Natale de Carolis *Paquiro*

BBC Singers

interval

Ravel
L'Heure espagnole (*sung in French*)   48'

Sarah Connolly *Concepción*
Charles Castronovo *Gonzalve*
Jean-Paul Fouchécourt *Torquemada*
Natale de Carolis *Ramiro*
Peter Rose *Don Inigo Gomez*

BBC Philharmonic
Gianandrea Noseda *conductor*

The BBC Philharmonic's new Principal
Conductor (*see pages 80–83*) presents
a special double bill of Spanish operas:
Granados's Goya-inspired fantasy about
the tangled love-lives of a goodtime girl,
a soldier and a toreador (*see page 7*) is
paired with Basque-born Ravel's risqué
comedy about a sex-starved Spanish
wife's race against time (*see page 20*).

This concert will be broadcast on BBC4

💬 **6.00pm Poetry Prom**
See page 133

PROM 19
Saturday 3 August
7.00pm – c9.05pm
Price Code **A**

NOTE TIME

Albéniz, arr. Rodion Shchedrin
Two Tangos   9'

Shostakovich
Violin Concerto No. 1   29'

interval

Rakhmaninov
Symphony No. 2   50'

Ilya Gringolts violin

BBC Philharmonic
Vassily Sinaisky conductor

Ilya Gringolts

Rodion Shchedrin gives a Russian twist to Spanish tangos by Albéniz, and Radio 3 New Generation Artist Ilya Gringolts negotiates the virtuosity of Shostakovich's First Violin Concerto. The BBC Philharmonic and its Principal Guest Conductor close the concert with Rakhmaninov's glorious Romantic symphony.

PROM 20
Saturday 3 August
10.00pm – c11.30pm
Price Code **D**

LATE NIGHT

Late-night Flamenco

José Mercé and Company

José Mercé

No music claims a more elemental appeal to the soul than the Spanish *cante jondo*, which has inspired centuries of music-making. One of the leading new stars of the flamenco world comes to London following his debut at WOMAD last year for a show which will combine passion and sophistication.

There will be no interval

PROM 21
Sunday 4 August
6.30pm – c10.00pm
Price Code **B**

NOTE TIME

Bach
St Matthew Passion
(sung in German)   175'

John Mark Ainsley *Evangelist*
Michael Volle *Christus*
Carolyn Sampson *soprano*
Susan Gritton *soprano*
Diana Moore *mezzo-soprano*
Robin Blaze *counter-tenor*
Werner Güra *tenor*
Stephan Loges *baritone*
Brindley Sherratt *bass*

Choristers of Southwark Cathedral
Choir of the English Concert
New London Chamber Choir
English Concert
Trevor Pinnock *conductor*

One of Trevor Pinnock's final collaborations as director of his English Concert, which he founded nearly three decades ago, brings the band together with an outstanding British Evangelist and German Christus for Bach's monumental meditation on Christ's suffering and death.

There will be one interval

💬 **5.00pm Pre-Prom Talk** (RAH)
Nicholas Anderson on Bach's *St Matthew Passion*

PROM 22
Monday 5 August
7.30pm – c9.40pm
Price Code **B**

Elgar
Froissart   14'

Anthony Payne
Visions and Journeys   c25'
BBC commission: world premiere

interval

Brahms
Piano Concerto No. 2
in B flat major   45'

Evgeny Kissin *piano*

BBC Symphony Orchestra
Sir Andrew Davis *conductor*

Evgeny Kissin

The Russian pianist Evgeny Kissin returns to the Proms in Brahms's fiendishly virtuosic Second Piano Concerto. The BBC SO and Sir Andrew Davis made the first recording of Anthony Payne's version of Elgar's unfinished Third Symphony, and they team up again for the first major new work from Payne since his Elgarian success (see page 44).

♪ **1.00pm Proms Chamber Music**
See pages 110–111

♪ **6.00pm Composer Portrait**
Anthony Payne. See page 134

PROM 23

Tuesday 6 August
7.00pm – c9.00pm
Price Code **A**

NOTE TIME

Panufnik
Sinfonia sacra   21'

Wagner
Tristan und Isolde – Prelude
and Liebestod   17'

interval

Strauss
Die Frau ohne Schatten – Suite   20'

Wagner
Götterdämmerung – excerpts
including Immolation Scene   c20'

Jane Eaglen *soprano*

**Royal Liverpool Philharmonic
Orchestra**
Gerard Schwarz *conductor*

Jane Eaglen

The Royal Liverpool Philharmonic visits the Proms with its new American Principal Conductor in his Proms debut. They present Wagnerian extracts with one of the leading Wagnerian sopranos of our time. A long-time champion of the music of Panufnik, Schwarz also gives us a rare chance to hear a suite drawn from Strauss's exotic fertility opera.

PROM 24

Tuesday 6 August
10.00pm – c11.20pm
Price Code **D**

LATE NIGHT

Giménez
La boda de Luis Alonso
– Intermedio   10'

Rodrigo, arr. Davis & Evans
Concierto de Aranjuez – Adagio   10'

John Harle
The Little Death Machine   c15'
world premiere

Falla, arr. Davis & Evans
El Amor brujo – Will-o'-the-Wisp   4'

Falla
El Amor brujo   25'

Ginesa Ortega *singer*
John Harle *saxophone*

Orchestra of St John's
John Lubbock *conductor*

Sketches of Spain: saxophonist John Harle reworks arrangements by legendary jazz trumpeter Miles Davis and Gil Evans of timeless Spanish works (see page 9); they frame a world premiere by Harle himself (see page 44). Falla's gypsy opera *Love, the Magician* (see page 8) is sung by an authentic flamenco singer.

There will be no interval

PROM 25

Wednesday 7 August
7.30pm – c9.35pm
Price Code **A**

Strauss
Don Juan   17'

Walton
Viola Concerto   27'

interval

Shostakovich
Symphony No. 5 in D minor   44'

Lars Anders Tomter *viola*

BBC Scottish Symphony Orchestra
Ion Marin *conductor*

The charismatic Romanian conductor Ion Marin has a newly-established relationship with the BBC Scottish Symphony Orchestra, and makes his Proms debut tonight in Strauss's colourful take on a Spanish tale and Shostakovich's symphonic 'reply to just criticism'. Centenary composer William Walton's Viola Concerto was premiered at the Proms in 1929 (see pages 52–54).

🔊 **6.00pm Pre-Prom Talk** (RAH)
Humphrey Burton on Walton

PROM 26

Thursday 8 August
7.30pm – c9.45pm
Price Code **A**

Revueltas
La noche de los mayas   30'

interval

Falla
La vida breve (*sung in Spanish*)   70'

Veronica Villarroel *Salud*
Felicity Palmer *Grandmother*
Jorge Pita *Paco*
Edgaras Montvidas *Voice in the Forge*
Leigh Melrose *Manuel*
Neal Davies *Uncle Sarvaor*

Pilar Rioja *flamenco dancer/castanets*
Alfonso Cid *flamenco singer*
José Luis Negrete, Antonio Muñoz
flamenco guitarists

London Voices
BBC Symphony Orchestra
Enrique Diemecke *conductor*

Silvestre Revueltas was the leading Mexican composer of the early 20th century; his wild, orgiastic celebration of ancient South American culture (see page 10) prefaces Falla's classic flamenco-flavoured evocation of Spain (see page 8). A Mexican conductor makes his Proms debut.

🔊 **6.00pm Pre-Prom Talk** (RAH)
Piers Burton-Page on *La vida breve*

PROM 27

Friday 9 August
7.00pm – c8.55pm
Price Code **A**

NOTE TIME

Rimsky-Korsakov Capriccio espagnol	15'
Falla Nights in the Gardens of Spain	23'
interval	
Rakhmaninov The Bells	36'

Pierre-Laurent Aimard piano

Irina Mataeva soprano
Daniil Shtoda tenor
William Dazeley baritone

Huddersfield Choral Society
BBC Symphony Chorus
BBC Scottish Symphony Orchestra
Martyn Brabbins conductor

Pierre-Laurent Aimard

Rimsky-Korsakov's colourfully Slavic view of Spain (see page 19) brings up the curtain on Falla's only full-scale concerto, played by a leading French pianist. Rakhmaninov's campanological cantata is based on Edgar Allan Poe's last published poems (see page 67).

PROM 28

Friday 9 August
10.00pm – c11.20pm
Price Code **E**

LATE NIGHT

Vivaldi Il Giustino – Sinfonia in C major	7'
Galuppi Concerto a 4 in G major	7'
Vivaldi Sinfonia in G minor for strings and continuo, RV 157	8'
Dorilla in Tempe – Sinfonia in C major	7'
The Four Seasons	38'

Giuliano Carmignola violin

Venice Baroque Orchestra
Andrea Marcon director

A highly-praised new Italian period-instrument orchestra prefaces Vivaldi's famous *Four Seasons* with lesser-known works by the 'Red Priest', and a concerto by Baldassare Galuppi, known as 'Il Buranello' after the Venetian island on which he was born.

There will be no interval

This concert will be broadcast on BBC1

PROM 29

Saturday 10 August
7.30pm – c9.40pm
Price Code **A**

Rossini The Barber of Seville – Overture; 'Largo al factotum'	13'
Mozart The Marriage of Figaro – 'Se vuol ballare'	3'
Don Giovanni – 'Deh vieni alla finestra'	3'
Haydn Piano Concerto in D major, Hob. XVIII:11	18'
interval	
Arriaga Los esclavos felices – Overture	8'
Ravel Don Quichotte à Dulcinée	7'
Mozart Symphony No. 39 in E flat major	29'

Sir Thomas Allen baritone

English Chamber Orchestra
Ralf Gothóni conductor/piano

Framed by classic works by Haydn and Mozart, a distinguished British baritone sings arias from Italian operas set in Spain, plus songs Ravel wrote for a film of Cervantes's *Don Quixote*. A genuinely Spanish overture is added by the ECO under its Principal Conductor.

PROM 30

Sunday 11 August
7.30pm – c9.05pm
Price Code **C**

Mahler Symphony No. 8 in E flat major, 'Symphony of a Thousand'	81'

Christine Brewer soprano
Soile Isokoski soprano
Rosemary Joshua soprano
Birgit Remmert mezzo-soprano
Jane Henschel mezzo-soprano
Jon Villars tenor
Peter Mattei baritone
John Relyea bass

City of Birmingham Symphony Youth Chorus
Toronto Children's Chorus
Sydney Philharmonia Choirs
London Symphony Chorus
City of Birmingham Symphony Chorus
National Youth Orchestra of Great Britain
Sir Simon Rattle conductor

Sir Simon Rattle conducts Mahler's massive 'Symphony of a Thousand' for the first time with the youth orchestra to which he himself belonged as a teenager (see page 68). A starry international cast is supported by choruses from three continents.

There will be no interval

This concert will be broadcast on BBC2

🗩 **6.00pm Pre-Prom Talk** (RCM)
Donald Mitchell on Mahler's Eighth

PROM 31
Monday 12 August
7.00pm – c10.15pm
Price Code **C**

Weber
Euryanthe (*sung in German;*
semi-staged)   153'

Anne Schwanewilms *Euryanthe*
Lauren Flanigan *Eglantine*
John Daszak *Adolar*
Pavlo Hunka *Lysiart*
Clive Bayley *King Louis VI*

Glyndebourne Chorus
Orchestra of the Age
of Enlightenment
Mark Elder *conductor*

Glyndebourne's revival of Weber's
'grand heroic Romantic opera' (*see*
page 69) marks the culmination of
Mark Elder's exploration of the
19th-century operatic repertoire
with the Orchestra of the Age of
Enlightenment. The cast of this
summer's Glyndebourne Festival
staging (directed by Richard Jones
with designs by John MacFarlane)
is led by Anne Schwanewilms.

There will be one interval

♪ **1.00pm Proms Chamber Music**
See pages 110–111

💬 **5.30pm Pre-Prom Talk** (RAH)
John Warrack on *Euryanthe*

PROM 32
Tuesday 13 August
7.30pm – c9.40pm
Price Code **B**

The Coronation
of King George II

The music performed at Westminster
Abbey on 11 October 1727

Part 1   40'

interval

Part 2   55'

Choir of the King's Consort
King's Consort
Robert King *conductor*

Following his spectacular reconstruction
of *Lo Sposalizio*, the ceremonial wedding
of Venice to the Adriatic, Robert King
returns with another reconstruction,
especially appropriate in the Queen's
Golden Jubilee Year. Handel's Coronation
Anthems (including *Zadok the Priest*)
and earlier anthems by Tallis, Gibbons,
Purcell and Blow are among the glorious
ceremonial pieces still considered fit for
a king (*see pages 36–38*).

💬 **6.00pm Pre-Prom Talk** (RAH)
Robert King in conversation with
Edward Blakeman

PROM 33 ➔
Wednesday 14 August
7.00pm – c9.10pm
Price Code **A**

Varèse
Intégrales   11'

Pierre Boulez
Le visage nuptial   30'

interval

Pierre Boulez
Le soleil des eaux   10'

Stravinsky
Petrushka (1911 version)   34'

Françoise Pollet *soprano*
Susan Parry *mezzo-soprano*

BBC Singers
BBC Symphony Orchestra
Pierre Boulez *conductor*

Pierre
Boulez

Pierre Boulez returns to
the BBC SO with his
early pair of cantatas on
verses by René Char,
framing them with one
of the seminal works
of the French-American composer
Edgard Varèse, and Stravinsky's
groundbreaking ballet score – of
which Boulez's interpretation has
become a modern classic.

♪ **5.30pm Composer Portrait**
Pierre Boulez. See page 134

PROM 34
Wednesday 14 August
10.00pm – c11.20pm
Price Code **D**

Elgar
Introduction and Allegro   14'

Imogen Holst, Oldham,
Tippett, Lennox Berkeley,
Britten, Searle, Walton
Variations on an Elizabethan Theme
(Sellinger's Round)   17'

Vaughan Williams
Fantasia on a Theme of
Thomas Tallis   15'

Tippett
Fantasia on a Theme of Corelli   16'

Australian Chamber Orchestra
Richard Tognetti *violin/director*

BT Scottish Ensemble
Clio Gould *violin/director*

Two virtuoso string groups from
opposite ends of the earth team
up to perform three classics of the
string repertoire which show British
composers interacting with the music
of the past. The BT Scottish Ensemble
adds a set of variations composed for
the Aldeburgh Festival in the year of
the Queen's Coronation.

There will be no interval

PROM 35

Thursday 15 August
7.00pm – c9.00pm
Price Code **A**

NOTE TIME

Nielsen
Saul and David – Preludes to
Acts 2 and 4   9'

Schumann
Piano Concerto in A minor   30'

interval

Sibelius
The Swan of Tuonela   10'

Symphony No. 1 in E minor   38'

Lars Vogt piano

BBC National Orchestra of Wales
Joseph Swensen conductor

Joseph Swensen, Principal Guest
Conductor of the BBC NOW, has a
close affinity with the music of Sibelius
and here presents the Finnish
composer's First Symphony and elegiac
Swan of Tuonela. He is joined by the
young German pianist Lars Vogt for a
rhapsodic Romantic concerto, prefaced
by music from Danish composer
Carl Nielsen's Old Testament opera.

PROM 36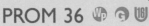

Friday 16 August
7.30pm – c9.30pm
Price Code **B**

Strauss
Don Quixote   42'

interval

Dvořák
Symphony No. 9 in E minor,
'From the New World'   42'

Truls Mørk cello
Paul Silverthorne viola

London Symphony Orchestra
Mariss Jansons conductor

Truls Mørk

Mariss Jansons makes a
welcome return, at the
helm of the LSO for the
first time at the Proms.
Dvořák's homesick salute
to the New World is
prefaced by Strauss's colourful
depiction of the quixotic adventures of
Cervantes's legendary Spanish knight.

6.00pm **Poetry Prom**
See page 133

PROM 37

Saturday 17 August
7.30pm – c9.50pm
Price Code **B**

Rodgers, orch. Spialek
Babes in Arms – Overture   5'

Rodgers, orch. R. R. Bennett
Victory at Sea – Suite   23'

interval

Rodgers & Hammerstein
Oklahoma! (concert version)   75'

Maureen Lipman Aunt Eller
Lisa Vroman Laurey
Klea Blackhurst Ado Annie
Tim Flavin Will
Brent Barrett Curley

Maida Vale Singers
BBC Concert Orchestra
David Charles Abell conductor

The first collaboration between
composer Richard Rodgers and lyricist
Oscar Hammerstein II broke both new
ground and box-office records. In this
special concert version to celebrate the
Rodgers centenary (see pages 58–59),
Maureen Lipman reprises her role from
the recent National Theatre production
with an all-star cast.

This concert will be broadcast on BBC2

6.00pm **Pre-Prom Talk** (RCM)
Sheridan Morley on Oklahoma!

PROM 38

Sunday 18 August
3.30pm – c5.45pm
Price Code **C**

NOTE TIME

Programme to include:

Wagner
Die Walküre – Wotan's Farewell

Strauss
Capriccio – final scene

Duets by **Donizetti, Gershwin,
Lehár** and **Mozart**

interval

A selection of songs and duets
from theatre and film

Renée Fleming soprano
Bryn Terfel bass-baritone

Orchestra of Welsh National Opera

Renée Fleming

Bryn Terfel

Two of the singers most
in demand around the
world – Bryn Terfel, rugby
fan and star of the 1994
Last Night, and Renée
Fleming, who thrilled the
Proms last year in early
Mozart and late Strauss –
combine for a unique
event to present music
from both sides of their
repertoire, opera and
musical theatre.

PROM 39

Sunday 18 August
8.00pm – c10.05pm
Price Code **A**

NOTE TIME

Rodion Shchedrin
Carmen Suite – excerpts   c20'

Ravel
Tzigane   10'

Sarasate
Zigeunerweisen   10'

interval

Prokofiev
Symphony No. 5 in B flat major   44'

Leonidas Kavakos violin

BBC Symphony Orchestra
Leonard Slatkin conductor

Leonidas Kavakos

The magnificent Fifth Symphony of Prokofiev is prefaced by dazzling Spanish postcards from Ravel and Sarasate (the violinist-composer who also commissioned the Lalo concerto heard on the First Night), as well as by Shchedrin's jovial take on themes from Bizet's *Carmen* (see pages 17–21).

PROM 40

Monday 19 August
7.30pm – c9.40pm
Price Code **A**

Janáček, arr. Tognetti
String Quartet No. 1, 'The Kreutzer
Sonata'   17'

Peter Sculthorpe
Nourlangie   19'

interval

Walton
Sonata for Strings (arr. from String
Quartet in A minor)   28'

Shostakovich
Concerto in C minor for piano,
trumpet and strings   22'

John Williams guitar

Olli Mustonen piano
Alison Balsom trumpet

Australian Chamber Orchestra
Richard Tognetti director

The Australian Chamber Orchestra presents two arrangements from string quartets, including one by Walton that was premiered in Australia, along with Shostakovich's fizzy early double concerto. Australian composer Peter Sculthorpe wrote *Nourlangie* especially for the leading guitarist John Williams.

♪ **1.00pm Proms Chamber Music**
See pages 110–111

💬 **6.00pm Pre-Prom Talk** (RAH)
Members of the ACO in conversation with Christopher Cook

PROM 41

Tuesday 20 August
7.00pm – c9.10pm
Price Code **A**

NOTE TIME

Gershwin
Cuban Overture   10'

Copland
Latin American Sketches   11'

Arias from
Rossini The Barber of Seville
Mozart Don Giovanni
Bizet Carmen   c12'

Turina
Danzas fantásticas   17'

interval

Revueltas
Sensemayá   6'

Zarzuela arias and Mexican popular
songs, including
Lara Granada   c15'

Copland
El salón México   11'

Ramón Vargas tenor

BBC Concert Orchestra
Barry Wordsworth conductor

Ramón Vargas

A scintillating Spanish and Latin programme by composers from both sides of the Atlantic, featuring popular arias from Spanish-themed operas and *zarzuelas* sung by a stylish Mexican tenor.

PROM 42

Tuesday 20 August
10.00pm – c11.30pm
Price Code **E**

LATE NIGHT

**John Williams and Friends –
Impressions of Africa**

Programme to include:

Trad.
Mazava (Madagascar)

John Williams
Musha musiki (Zimbabwe)

Trad./Djessou Mory Kante
Djandjon (Mali)

John Williams
Malinké guitars (Senegal)

Trad.
Cuban 'danzón'

and music by **Francis Bebey**

John Williams guitar
John Etheridge acoustic steel-strung guitar
Richard Harvey flutes/whistles
Chris Laurence double bass
Paul Clarvis hand-drums & percussion

John Williams returns with his quintet to perform a colourful collection of music from Africa and the Caribbean.

There will be no interval

Every Prom live on BBC Radio 3 and www.bbc.co.uk/proms

PROM 43

Wednesday 21 August
7.30pm – c9.45pm
Price Code **C**

Mozart
Divertimento in D major, K136   12'

Beethoven
Violin Concerto in D major   42'

interval

Mozart
Serenade in D major, K320,
'Posthorn'   39'

Joshua Bell *violin*

Camerata Salzburg
Sir Roger Norrington *conductor*

Joshua Bell

The Camerata Salzburg is celebrating its half-century this year. Under its Chief Conductor, Sir Roger Norrington, it performs two of Mozart's most inventive entertainments, and is joined by the pre-eminent American violinist Joshua Bell in Beethoven's only concerto for the instrument, which Bell has just recorded for the first time.

PROM 44 🔢 ⚔

Thursday 22 August
7.30pm – c9.30pm
Price Code **C**

Bartók
Music for Strings, Percussion
and Celesta   30'

interval

Ravel
Piano Concerto in G major   22'

Debussy
La mer   24'

Martha Argerich *piano*

Gustav Mahler Jugendorchester
Claudio Abbado *conductor*

Martha Argerich

One of Europe's most exciting youth orchestras is joined by Claudio Abbado for a concert of 20th-century classics. Proms favourite Martha Argerich returns for what promises to be a memorable performance of Ravel's light-hearted, jazz-tinged concerto.

PROM 45 🔢 🔢 🔢

Friday 23 August
7.30pm – c9.40pm
Price Code **A**

Stravinsky
Le chant du rossignol   20'

Berg
Violin Concerto   27'

interval

Ravel
Pavane pour une infante défunte   6'

Sibelius
Symphony No. 5 in E flat major   30'

Christian Tetzlaff *violin*

Orchestre National de Lyon
David Robertson *conductor*

After last year's appearance with the BBC Symphony Orchestra, David Robertson brings his own French orchestra to the Proms for the first time in works composed in memory of a princess and an angel, and in evocations of nightingales and swans.

PROM 46 🔢

Saturday 24 August
7.30pm – c10.15pm
Price Code **C**

Musorgsky
Boris Godunov (1869 version)
(sung in Russian)   130'

Vladimir Ognovenko *Boris*
Alexander Morozov *Pimen*
Konstantin Pluzhnikov *Shuisky*
Alexei Steblianko *Grigori ('Dmitri')*
Evgeny Akimov *Simpleton*
Fedor Kuznetsov *Varlaam*
Nikolai Gassiev *Missail*
Nadezhda Vasilieva *Hostess of the Inn*

**Chorus and Orchestra
of the Kirov Opera**
Valery Gergiev *conductor*

The full forces of St Petersburg's Mariinsky Theatre visit the Proms with their visionary conductor Valery Gergiev for a special weekend of concerts displaying three sides of their activities. In the first concert, they give a concert performance of the original 1869 version of Musorgsky's *Boris Godunov*, a tragic chronicle of a tortured Tsar and a troubled people (see page 70).

There will be one interval

🗨 **6.00pm Pre-Prom Talk** (RCM)
Piers Burton-Page on *Boris Godunov*

PROM 47

Sunday 25 August
1.00pm – c4.10pm
Price Code **A**

NOTE
TIME

Sofia Gubaidulina
Passion and Resurrection of Jesus
Christ according to St John
UK premiere

St John Passion   95'

interval

St John Easter   58'

Natalia Korneva *soprano*
Viktor Lutsiuk *tenor*
Fedor Mozhaev *baritone*
Gennady Bezzubenkov *bass*

St Petersburg Chamber Choir
Chorus and Orchestra of
the Kirov Opera
Valery Gergiev *conductor*

Sofia Gubaidulina's *St John Passion* was
one of four Passions commissioned for
a unique celebration of the Bach year
in 2000 (see page 71). Gubaidulina
interleaves passages of the gospel in
Russian with verses from the Book of
Revelation, creating a fierce, ritualistic
passion that prefigures the Apocalypse.
The added second part, telling the
story of the Resurrection, was
acclaimed at its first performance in
Germany earlier this year.

💬 **11.30am Pre-Prom Talk** (RAH)
Gerard McBurney on Gubaidulina

PROM 48

Sunday 25 August
8.00pm – c10.10pm
Price Code **C**

NOTE
TIME

Prokofiev
Piano Concerto No. 3 in C major   29'

interval

Shostakovich
Symphony No. 4 in C minor   63'

Alexander Toradze *piano*

Kirov Orchestra
Valery Gergiev *conductor*

The Kirov Orchestra completes its trio
of concerts with a pairing of Prokofiev's
most popular piano concerto and the
titanic symphony that Shostakovich
himself withdrew, fearing that its
meanings might be misconstrued
in the Stalinesque political climate
of 1930s Russia.

This concert will be broadcast on BBC2

PROM 49

Monday 26 August
7.30pm – c9.45pm
Price Code **C**

Bach
Suite No. 3 in D major, BWV 1068   20'

Beethoven
Piano Concerto No. 2
in B flat major   30'

interval

Janáček
Capriccio   22'

Haydn
Symphony No. 88 in G major   22'

Chamber Orchestra of Europe
András Schiff *piano/conductor*

András Schiff, well known
as a leading pianist, is also
gaining recognition as a
conductor. He appears
here with one of Europe's
finest orchestras, directing
from the keyboard in Beethoven's
youthful piano concerto and Janáček's
quirky *Capriccio*, and – as a dedicated
exponent of Bach on modern
instruments – conducting the famous
Third Suite.

András Schiff

🎵 **1.00pm Proms Chamber Music**
See pages 110–111

PROM 50

Tuesday 27 August
7.00pm – c9.00pm
Price Code **C**

NOTE
TIME

Stravinsky
Pulcinella (complete)   38'

interval

Rossini, arr. Respighi
La boutique fantasque   21'

Respighi
The Pines of Rome   22'

Sonia Ganassi *mezzo-soprano*
Kenneth Tarver *tenor*
Michele Pertusi *bass*

Royal Concertgebouw Orchestra
Riccardo Chailly *conductor*

Riccardo Chailly makes a
welcome return to the
Proms for a pair of
concerts with the Royal
Concertgebouw
Orchestra. Twentieth-
century arrangements of earlier music
by Pergolesi (and others) and Rossini
lead to a performance of Respighi's
sumptuous evocation of the sights and
sounds of the Eternal City.

Riccardo Chailly

💬 **5.30pm Pre-Prom Talk** (RCM)
Members of the Royal Concertgebouw
Orchestra in conversation with
Sue Knussen

PROM 51

Tuesday 27 August
10.00pm – c11.30pm
Price Code **D**

 LATE NIGHT

Osvaldo Golijov
Last Round   15'

Simon Holt
Canciones   25'

Falla
Master Peter's Puppet Show
(*sung in Spanish*)   30'

Jean Rigby *mezzo-soprano*

Yvette Bonner *soprano*
Timothy Robinson *tenor*
Jonathan Lemalu *bass-baritone*

**Birmingham Contemporary
Music Group**
Alexander Briger *conductor*

The music of the Argentine composer
Osvaldo Golijov makes its Proms debut
alongside Simon Holt's Lorca settings in
this late-night concert performed by
Birmingham's acclaimed new music
group. Falla's delightful version of an
episode from *Don Quixote* was
composed as a puppet-show-within-a-
puppet-show for the marionette
theatre of the Princesse de Polignac
in 1920s Paris (see page 8).

There will be no interval

PROM 52

Wednesday 28 August
7.30pm – c9.20pm
Price Code **C**

Mahler
Symphony No. 3 in D minor   99'

Michelle DeYoung *mezzo-soprano*
London Symphony Chorus
(women's voices)
Trinity Boys Choir

Royal Concertgebouw Orchestra
Riccardo Chailly *conductor*

Michelle DeYoung

The music of Mahler has
been at the heart of
Riccardo Chailly's work
with the Concertgebouw,
and represents the latest
flowering of a tradition
that reaches back as far as Willem
Mengelberg, the orchestra's Principal
Conductor from 1895 to 1941 and
one of Mahler's earliest champions.
Here Chailly presents a rare chance
to hear the massive Third Symphony,
the centrepiece of the composer's
early triptych of vocal symphonies
(see page 68).

There will be no interval

PROM 53 ✓

Thursday 29 August
7.30pm – c9.45pm
Price Code **A**

Berlioz
The Trojans – Prologue (Lamento)
and Trojan March   9'

Thomas Adès
America   15'

interval

Sibelius
Kullervo Symphony   72'

Susan Bickley *mezzo-soprano*
Raimo Laukka *baritone*

Crouch End Festival Chorus
London Symphony Chorus
(men's voices)
BBC Symphony Orchestra
Thomas Adès *conductor*

Already familiar as a composer and
pianist, Thomas Adès conducts a
complete Prom for the first time,
presenting not just his own New York
Philharmonic millennium commission –
setting a Mayan prophecy of impending
destruction – but also prophetic music
from Berlioz's epic opera, and Sibelius's
early choral symphony based on ancient
Finnish folklore (see page 72).

PROM 54

Friday 30 August
7.30pm – c9.45pm
Price Code **C**

Debussy
Ibéria   21'

Bartók
Piano Concerto No. 1   24'

interval

Prokofiev
Romeo and Juliet – excerpts   45'

Yefim Bronfman *piano*

Los Angeles Philharmonic
Esa-Pekka Salonen *conductor*

Yefim Bronfman

Yefim Bronfman returns to
the Proms, following his
triumph last year in
Beethoven's 'Emperor'
Concerto, with one of
America's finest orchestras
and its dynamic conductor, Esa-Pekka
Salonen. This team has recently
recorded the complete Bartók
concertos; they complement the
percussive First with excerpts from
Prokofiev's colourful Shakespearian
ballet score and Debussy's sensuous
impressions of Spain (see page 21).

💬 6.00pm **Poetry Prom**
See page 133

PROM 55

Saturday 31 August
7.30pm – c9.30pm
Price Code **C**

Shostakovich
Symphony No. 2 in B major, 'October'   20'

interval

Beethoven
Symphony No. 9 in D minor, 'Choral'   68'

Melanie Diener *soprano*
Paula Rasmussen *mezzo-soprano*
Robert Gambill *tenor*
Eike Wilm Schulte *bass*

BBC Symphony Chorus
Los Angeles Philharmonic
Esa-Pekka Salonen *conductor*

The traditional performance of Beethoven's life-affirming choral symphony falls this year to our visitors from Los Angeles. The concert contrasts unattainable ideals, and opens with Shostakovich's paean to the Russian October Revolution.

This concert will be broadcast on BBC2

PROM 56

Sunday 1 September
7.00pm – c9.45pm
Price Code **B**

NOTE TIME

Mendelssohn
Elijah (*sung in English*)   130'

Alastair Miles *Elijah*
Janice Watson *soprano*
Alice Coote *mezzo-soprano*
Kim Begley *tenor*

London Philharmonic Choir
Philharmonia Chorus
London Philharmonic Orchestra
Kurt Masur *conductor*

Kurt Masur

Mendelssohn's dramatic retelling of the story of one of the great Old Testament prophets (see *pages 28–31*) is conducted by Kurt Masur, a musician with Mendelssohn in his blood following his long association with the composer's own orchestra, the Leipzig Gewandhaus.

There will be one interval

💬 **5.30pm Pre-Prom Talk** (RAH)
Mark Lowther on *Elijah*

PROM 57

Monday 2 September
7.00pm – c9.05pm
Price Code **A**

NOTE TIME

Ives
A Symphony: New England Holidays   40'

interval

Mahler
Symphony No. 1 in D major   55'

London Chorus
BBC Symphony Orchestra
Ingo Metzmacher *conductor*

The young German conductor Ingo Metzmacher made his Proms debut two years ago with the British premiere of Henze's Ninth Symphony. Having made high-profile debuts with both the London Symphony and New York Philharmonic orchestras this season, he now returns to the Proms, pairing the fractured nostalgia of Ives's holiday collection with the turbulent eclecticism of Mahler's First Symphony.

♪ **1.00pm Proms Chamber Music**
See pages 110–111

💬 **5.30pm Pre-Prom Talk** (RCM)
Calum MacDonald on Charles Ives

PROM 58

Monday 2 September
10.00pm – c11.30pm
Price Code **D**

LATE NIGHT

Julian Anderson
Alhambra Fantasy   12'

Stravinsky
Abraham and Isaac   12'

Revueltas
Homenaje a Federico García Lorca   15'

George Crumb
Songs, Drones and Refrains of Death   30'

Sanford Sylvan *baritone*

Sinfonia 21
Martyn Brabbins *conductor*

Stravinsky's stark *Abraham and Isaac* forms a counterpoint to Britten's setting of the same biblical story, being performed in this afternoon's Proms Chamber Music concert at the V&A (see *page 111*). The season's Spanish theme is further explored in Lorca-inspired pieces by Revueltas and Crumb, and in Julian Anderson's evocation of the Alhambra Palace in Granada.

There will be no interval

PROM 59

Tuesday 3 September
7.30pm – c9.50pm
Price Code **C**

Hindemith
Symphonic Metamorphoses on
Themes of Weber   21'

Mozart
Piano Concerto No. 20 in D minor,
K466   31'

interval

Varèse
Amériques   24'

Ravel
Daphnis and Chloë – Suite No. 2   17'

Alfred Brendel piano

Munich Philharmonic Orchestra
James Levine conductor

James
Levine

James Levine makes his
belated Proms debut with
the Munich Philharmonic
Orchestra, presenting
contrasting French works
by the futuristic Varèse
and the nostalgic Ravel, alongside one
of Hindemith's best-loved scores,
a set of variations on tunes by the
composer of *Euryanthe*. Alfred
Brendel's annual appearances are
always highlights, and he here performs
Mozart's brooding *Sturm und Drang*-
inspired piano concerto.

PROM 60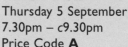

Wednesday 4 September
7.00pm – c8.55pm
Price Code **A**

NOTE TIME

Brahms
Violin Concerto in D major   38'

interval

Walton
Symphony No. 1   43'

James Ehnes violin

BBC National Orchestra of Wales
Richard Hickox conductor

James
Ehnes

Centenary composer
William Walton's First
Symphony is by common
consent his orchestral
masterpiece, and was
given its first complete
performance by the BBC Symphony
Orchestra (see pages 52–54). Richard
Hickox and his Welsh forces pair it
with Brahms's virtuosic concerto,
performed by a young Canadian
violinist making a welcome return to
the Proms.

PROM 61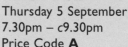

Wednesday 4 September
10.00pm – c11.30pm
Price Code **D**

LATE NIGHT

Walton
The Twelve   13'

Simon Bainbridge
Chant   18'
London premiere

Duruflé
Requiem   38'

Louise Winter mezzo-soprano
Roderick Williams baritone

BBC Singers
City of London Sinfonia
Stephen Cleobury conductor

We celebrate the centenary of Maurice
Duruflé's birth with a performance of
his best-known work (see page 55),
and the 50th birthday of Simon
Bainbridge with his BBC millennium
commission, *Chant* (see page 43).
Walton's Auden setting was composed
for Christ Church Cathedral, Oxford
(see pages 52–54).

There will be no interval

PROM 62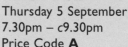

Thursday 5 September
7.30pm – c9.30pm
Price Code **A**

Debussy
Nocturnes   18'

Mozart
Piano Concerto No. 17 in G major,
K453   30'

interval

Stravinsky
The Rite of Spring   34'

Richard Goode piano

BBC Singers (women's voices)
BBC Philharmonic
Yan Pascal Tortelier conductor

The end of Yan Pascal Tortelier's
distinguished time as Chief Conductor
of the BBC Philharmonic (see pages
80–83) is marked by this performance
of Stravinsky's riotous ballet score.
Renowned Mozartian Richard Goode
returns in one of Mozart's sunniest
concertos.

PROM 63

Friday 6 September
7.30pm – c9.40pm
Price Code **A**

Marc-André Dalbavie
Color   17'
UK premiere

Barber
Violin Concerto   25'

interval

Tchaikovsky
Symphony No. 4 in F minor   43'

Midori *violin*

BBC Symphony Orchestra
Christoph Eschenbach *conductor*

After his triumph at the Proms last year, Christoph Eschenbach teams up for the first time with the BBC Symphony Orchestra for Tchaikovsky's tragic Fourth Symphony and the UK premiere of Marc-André Dalbavie's spectral *Color* (see page 43). Midori makes a long-awaited return in Barber's beautiful Violin Concerto.

🔊 **6.00pm Pre-Prom Talk** (RAH)
Marc-André Dalbavie

PROM 64

Saturday 7 September
7.30pm – c9.50pm
Price Code **A**

Moncayo
Huapango   6'

Galindo Dimas
Sones de Mariachi   10'

Falla, arr. Luciano Berio
Seven Popular Spanish Songs   12'

Piazzolla
Bandoneon Concerto   22'

interval

Piazzolla
Pieces for tango quartet   c15'

Tangazo for orchestra   15'

Ginastera
Estancia – Suite   12'

Ann Murray *mezzo-soprano*
Horacio Romo *bandoneon*

BBC Concert Orchestra
Miguel Harth-Bedoya *conductor*

The haunting music of Astor Piazzolla has travelled the world: its unique mixture of folk-based eloquence and inventiveness has made a huge impact on audiences. The young Peruvian Associate Conductor of the Los Angeles Philharmonic makes his London debut.

🔊 **5.45pm Audience Forum**
Share your views with representatives from the BBC and the Royal Albert Hall

PROM 65

Sunday 8 September
3.00pm – c4.30pm
Price Code **G**

NOTE TIME

Blue Peter Prom – Fiesta!
A colourful programme for all the family, to include:

Bizet
Carmen – orchestral excerpts   6'

Trad., arr. Michael Neaum
A la rurru niño (Lullaby)   4'

Sarasate
Carmen Fantasy – excerpts   c7'

Flamenco Music and Dance   c6'

Falla
The Three-Cornered Hat –
Final Dance   6'

interval

Damien Harron
Carnival of Rhythms   c8'
world premiere

Trad.
Jarabe tapatio (Mexican Hat Dance)   3'

Elmer Bernstein
The Magnificent Seven – Theme   4'

Matt Baker and Liz Barker *presenters*
Chloë Hanslip *violin*
Paco Peña and Friends *flamenco music and dance*
Backbeat *percussion quartet*
Islington Children's Music Group
BBC Philharmonic
Rumon Gamba *conductor*

This concert will be broadcast on BBC2

PROM 66

Sunday 8 September
7.00pm – c10.00pm
Price Code **B**

NOTE TIME

Handel
Samson   140'

Lisa Milne *Dalila*
Catherine Wyn-Rogers *Micha*
Thomas Randle *Samson*
Michael George *Manoah*
John Tomlinson *Harapha*

The Sixteen
Symphony of Harmony and Invention
Harry Christophers *conductor*

Thomas Randle

One of Handel's most powerful treatments of an Old Testament story (see pages 28–31), *Samson* contains some of the composer's most dramatic choruses and solos, including the well-loved soprano aria 'Let the bright Seraphim'.

There will be one interval

🔊 **5.30pm Pre-Prom Talk** (RAH)
Donald Burrows on *Samson*

PROM 67

Monday 9 September
7.00pm – c9.00pm
Price Code **B**

NOTE TIME

Strauss
Till Eulenspiegel   15'

Beethoven
Piano Concerto No. 4 in G major   34'

interval

Dvořák
Symphony No. 8 in G major   34'

Emanuel Ax *piano*

Philharmonia Orchestra
Christoph von Dohnányi *conductor*

Emanuel Ax

Emanuel Ax has become a firm favourite at the Proms, and tonight performs Beethoven's limpid Fourth Concerto. The concert opens with Strauss's rumbustious orchestral scherzo and ends with Dvořák's evergreen 'English' symphony.

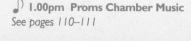
♪ 1.00pm **Proms Chamber Music**
See pages 110–111

PROM 68

Monday 9 September
10.00pm – c11.20pm
Price Code **D**

LATE NIGHT

The Genius of Renaissance Spain

Victoria
Missa pro victoria

interspersed with motets by
Morales, Guerrero, Escribano, Padilla and others

The Cardinall's Musick Consort and Players
Andrew Carwood *director*

Andrew Carwood and the Cardinall's Musick have specialised in early Spanish repertoire and here present a concert of music from the Iberian Peninsula, matching Victoria's exuberant 'Victory Mass' with richly polyphonic music by other Renaissance composers (see page 6).

There will be no interval

PROM 69

Tuesday 10 September
7.30pm – c9.40pm
Price Code **A**

Rakhmaninov
Piano Concerto No. 2 in C minor   33'

interval

Shostakovich
Symphony No. 8   61'

André Watts *piano*

BBC Symphony Orchestra
Leonard Slatkin *conductor*

André Watts

Two Russian masterpieces: American pianist André Watts returns to the Proms after a break of 15 years with Rakhmaninov's concerto, well known from the film *Brief Encounter*. It is paired with Shostakovich's monumental and anguished Eighth Symphony.

PROM 70

Wednesday 11 September
7.30pm – c9.20pm
Price Code **B**

Julian Anderson
Imagin'd Corners   9'
London premiere

Prokofiev
Violin Concerto No. 1   22'

interval

Nielsen
Symphony No. 5   37'

Elisabeth Batiashvili *violin*

City of Birmingham Symphony Orchestra
Sakari Oramo *conductor*

Elisabeth Batiashvili

Julian Anderson is Composer-in-Association to the CBSO, and his first work for them gives the orchestra's horn section a starring role (see page 43). Nielsen's masterpiece was written in the aftermath of the First World War and, appropriately for 11 September, celebrates the human ability to seek hope and renewal after tragedy. Elisabeth Batiashvili is an outstanding graduate from Radio 3's New Generation Artists scheme.

♪ 5.30pm **Composer Portrait**
Julian Anderson. See page 134

PROM 71

Thursday 12 September
7.30pm – c9.35pm
Price Code **B**

Haydn
Symphony No. 96 in D major,
'Miracle'   20'

interval

Bruckner
Symphony No. 4 in E flat major,
'Romantic'   70'

London Symphony Orchestra
Bernard Haitink conductor

Bernard Haitink, a leading Brucknerian,
makes his annual Proms appearance
this year with the LSO, prefacing
Bruckner's 'Romantic' Symphony with
a miraculous work from the London
years of the 'Father of the Symphony'.

PROM 72

Friday 13 September
7.30pm – c9.55pm
Price Code **B**

Tchaikovsky
Fantasy-Overture 'Romeo and Juliet' 22'

Musorgsky, orch. Shostakovich
Songs and Dances of Death   20'

interval

Mahler
Symphony No. 5   68'

Olga Borodina mezzo-soprano

Royal Philharmonic Orchestra
Daniele Gatti conductor

Olga
Borodina

Daniele Gatti has
performed Mahler's Fifth
Symphony across Europe
with the RPO. They open
their concert with an all-
Russian first half featuring
Tchaikovsky's passionate depiction of
Shakespeare's 'star-cross'd lovers' and
Shostakovich's pungent orchestration
of Musorgsky's morbidly spine-tingling
song-cycle, for which we welcome back
a leading Russian mezzo-soprano.

PROM 73

Saturday 14 September
7.30pm – c10.30pm
Price Code **F**

THE LAST NIGHT OF THE PROMS 2002

Walton
Anniversary fanfare;
March: Orb and Sceptre   8'

Walton, arr. Sargent
Henry V Suite (with narration)   15'

**Colin Matthews, Judith Weir,
Lukas Foss, Poul Ruders, David
Sawer, Michael Torke, Anthony
Payne, Magnus Lindberg**
Bright Cecilia: Variations on a Theme
by Purcell   c16'
*BBC Music Magazine commission:
world premiere*

Grieg
Piano Concerto in A minor   30'

interval

Elgar
Pomp and Circumstance March No. 1
in D major   5'

Parry
I Was Glad   8'

Sullivan
The Yeomen of the Guard –
Overture   5'

Rodgers
A centenary sequence to include:
Cinderella Waltz; Songs   c20'

Wood
Fantasia on British Sea-Songs   15'

Parry, orch. Elgar
Jerusalem   2'

orch. Britten
The National Anthem   2'

Samuel West *speaker**
Leif Ove Andsnes *piano*
Audra McDonald *soprano*

BBC Singers
BBC Symphony Chorus
BBC Symphony Orchestra
Leonard Slatkin conductor

Audra
McDonald

After the radical changes
to last year's Last Night,
Leonard Slatkin brings
back tradition refreshed
with a programme that
celebrates the Queen's
Golden Jubilee, the contrasting
centenaries of William Walton and
Richard Rodgers, and the first decade
of *BBC Music Magazine* (see page 46).
One of the greatest young virtuosos
plays one of the most popular of
concertos, and we join Proms in the
Park events around the country –
including, for the first time, in Northern
Ireland – as music once more brings us
together.

* *subject to availability*

*This concert will be broadcast on BBC2 (Part 1)
and BBC1 (Part 2)*

BBC Proms in the Park

The BBC presents the seventh season of Proms in the Park, bringing the traditional atmosphere of the Last Night of the Proms to audiences in London, Belfast and Gateshead. All three concerts culminate in live big-screen link-ups with the Royal Albert Hall

BBC Proms in the Park, London

International opera stars Lesley Garrett and José Cura plus the amazing African *a cappella* choir Ladysmith Black Mambazo lead the celebrity line-up joining the BBC Concert Orchestra under conductor Robin Stapleton for the main part of the evening's entertainment, hosted yet again by the inimitable Terry Wogan.

Saturday 14 September
Hyde Park. Gates open 4.00pm; entertainment on stage from 5.30pm

THE ROYAL PARKS

Tickets: £17.00, available now by post/fax using the Booking Form facing page 122, by phone on 0870 899 8100 (24 hours, national rate) or online via www.bbc.co.uk/proms.
A £2.00 transaction fee applies.

Corporate hospitality facilities are available. Call Charles Webb on 01484 435569.

CBBC Prom in the Park, London

A fun-filled family afternoon featuring top acts from the charts, stars and friends from favourite CBBC programmes plus the musicians of the BBC Philharmonic conducted by Rumon Gamba, winner of the 1998 BBC Young Musicians Conductors' Workshop.

Sunday 15 September
Hyde Park, London. Gates open 12.30pm; entertainment on stage from 2.00pm

Tickets: £11.00 (adults), £7 (children 3–16; under-3s free), available now by post/fax using the Booking Form facing page 122, by phone on 0870 899 8001 (24 hours, national rate) or online via www.bbc.co.uk/proms.
A £2.00 transaction fee applies.

BBC Blue Planet Prom in the Park, London

Swim with the dolphins, plunge with the whales, immerse yourself in the music and pictures of the BBC's astonishing underwater natural history series, performed live by the BBC Concert Orchestra and the Choir of Magdalen College, Oxford, conducted by composer George Fenton and narrated by the series' presenter David Attenborough and producer Alastair Fothergill.
In association with BBC Music

Sunday 15 September
Hyde Park, London. Gates open 7.30pm

Tickets: £15.00, available now by post/fax using the Booking Form facing page 122, by phone on 0870 899 9990 (24 hours, national rate) or online via www.bbc.co.uk/proms.
A £2.00 transaction fee applies.

Note: tickets for all BBC Proms in the Park, London, can also be bought in person (no transaction fee) at the BBC Shops in Portland Place, W1 and at Bush House, The Strand, WC2.

RENAULT – Event sponsor of Proms in the Park, London, and CBBC Prom in the Park

BBC Proms in the Park, Belfast

Belfast joins the Last Night festivities for the very first time. Live open-air concert with the Ulster Orchestra in the surroundings of City Hall in Belfast's Donegal Square.

Saturday 14 September
Donegal Square, Belfast.

For further information, please call 08700 100 300

BBC Proms in the Park, Gateshead

Baltic Square joins the Last Night festivities for a second year with a Tyneside musical feast featuring percussionist Evelyn Glennie and the Northern Sinfonia.

Saturday 14 September
Baltic Square, Gateshead. Gates open 6.30pm; concert begins 7.30pm

Tickets: £15.00, available now from Freephone 0800 953 0070

Please note: all BBC Proms in the Park events are outdoors and tickets are unreserved. The use of chairs is discouraged since it obstructs the view of others, but if you find it necessary because of limited mobility, please be considerate to your neighbours. In the interest of safety, please do not bring glass items, barbecues or flaming torches.

Proms Chamber Music

Mondays at 1.00pm
Lecture Theatre, Victoria and Albert Museum
Broadcast live on BBC Radio 3
and repeated the following Sunday at 1.00pm

The BBC Proms and the Victoria & Albert Museum continue their popular collaboration, presenting eight Monday lunchtime concerts highlighting Proms artists, themes and anniversaries in the intimate setting of the Lecture Theatre at the V&A, a short walk from the Royal Albert Hall.

How to Book
All tickets £6.00.
Advance booking is advised.

Before the day of the concert all bookings should be made with the Royal Albert Hall Box Office, *either* using the priority Booking Form (*facing page 122*), the Online Ticket Request system (at www.bbc.co.uk/proms) *or* by telephone or in person (from Monday 17 June).

On the day of the concert tickets can only be bought (*subject to availability*) at the V&A, Exhibition Road entrance (*see map on page 114*).

Performing Art
12.15pm – c12.35pm
Recorded for broadcast on BBC Radio 3 as interval features during evening Proms

Once again, arts broadcaster Christopher Cook unveils some of the riches of the V&A collection in conversation with guest experts from the museum. Each talk will focus on a particular object that relates to the music being performed – as, for example, the 15th-century Spanish tin-glazed earthenware bowl from Malaga (*below*).

Performing Art talks are free to Proms Chamber Music ticket-holders.

Note that admission to the V&A is now free and that the museum and its restaurant are open from 10.00am.

For details of the BBC Proms Lecture, Poetry Proms, Proms Composer Portraits and Pre-Prom Talks, see pages 131–134.

PCM 1
Monday 22 July
1.00pm – c2.00pm

Ibert
Le jardinier de Samos   12'

Walton
Façade   40'

Nash Ensemble
Philippa Davies *flute*
Richard Hosford *clarinet*
Mark David *trumpet*
Martin Robertson *alto saxophone*
Marianne Thorsen *violin*
Paul Watkins *cello*
Simon Limbrick *percussion*

Prunella Scales *reciter*
Samuel West *reciter*
Martyn Brabbins *conductor*

Walton's eternally youthful settings of Edith Sitwell's zany poetry launch the season in style, celebrating the composer's centenary. Jacques Ibert, an equally 'bright young thing' from across the Channel, contributes a curtain-raising pot-pourri of incidental music for a similar instrumental ensemble.

PCM 2
Monday 29 July
1.00pm – c2.00pm

D. Scarlatti
Sonatas: in E major, K380; in A minor, K3; in C major, K514   10'

Chabrier
Habanera   4'
Danse villageoise   4'

Mompou
Música callada – selections   8'
Paisajes Nos. 1 and 2   9'

Ravel
Miroirs – 'Une barque sur l'océan' and 'Alborada del gracioso'   14'

Alexandre Tharaud *piano*

Alexandre Tharaud

Spain and echoes of Spain resonate in an imaginative recital by a brilliant young French pianist. Heady evocations from Chabrier and Ravel are tempered by the cool, reflective poise of Mompou and the gestural restraint of Domenico Scarlatti.

PCM 3
Monday 5 August
1.00pm – c2.00pm

Falla
Concerto for harpsichord and five instruments   14'

Poulenc
Sextet for piano and wind   18'

Joseph Phibbs
La noche arrolladora   c12'
BBC commission: world premiere

Piazzolla
Tango Seis   6'

English Chamber Orchestra Ensemble
Ian Brown *harpsichord/piano*
Stephanie Gonley *violin*
Josephine Knight *cello*
William Bennett *flute*
John Anderson *oboe*
Anthony Pike *clarinet*
Richard Berry *horn*
Julie Price *bassoon*

Fiery and flamboyant, the chamber concerto by featured composer Manuel de Falla reinvented the harpsichord for the 20th century. Young British composer Joseph Phibbs takes up the challenge with a new work for the same forces, partly inspired by the poetry of Pablo Neruda, while Poulenc and Piazzolla add their own glittering colours to the mix.

PCM 4
Monday 12 August
1.00pm – c2.00pm

Peñalosa
Missa 'L'Homme armé'   25'

interspersed with secular
instrumental and vocal works:

Anon., arr. Morton
L'Homme armé   3'

La Torre
Danza Alta 'La Spagna'   2'
Dime triste coraçón   3'

Pisador
Dezilde al cavallero
y su vuelta   2'

Gombert
Dezilde al cavallero   3'

Anon
Diferencias sobre 'Conde
Claros'   4'

Cabezón
Diferencias sobre 'El canto del
cavallero'   4'

**Orchestra of the
Renaissance**
Richard Cheetham director

Spain's Age of Chivalry lives
again in music for the 15th-
century ceremonies of the
Order of the Golden Fleece
and the feast-day of the
Archangel Michael. The
centrepiece is a rare
performance of the first
surviving Spanish Mass to be
based on the popular song
L'Homme armé.

PCM 5
Monday 19 August
1.00pm – c2.00pm

Haydn
Arianna a Naxos   17'

Bizet
Chanson d'avril   3'
Vieille chanson   4'
Absence   4'
Adieux de l'hôtesse arabe   5'

Wolf
Spanisches Liederbuch –
selection   16'

Alice Coote mezzo-soprano
Julius Drake piano

Alice
Coote

Drama and
desire interlock
in a wide-
ranging vocal
recital from one
of the brightest
stars of the Radio 3 New
Generation Artists. Haydn at
his most affecting and Bizet
at his most beguiling prepare
the way for a kaleidoscope of
moods in Wolf's unique
settings of 16th- and 17th-
century sacred and secular
Spanish texts.

PCM 6
Monday 26 August
1.00pm – c2.00pm

Duruflé
Prelude, Recitative and
Variations, Op. 3   14'

Villa-Lobos
Assobio a jato   11'

Weber
Trio in G minor, Op. 63   22'

Emily Beynon flute
Gregor Horsch cello
Andrew West piano

Principal players of the visiting
Royal Concertgebouw
Orchestra bring a fresh spin
to the traditional piano trio
line-up. Duruflé's centenary is
marked with his solitary, richly
Romantic chamber work,
alongside Weber's classically
lyrical score and some exotic
seasoning from Latin America.

PCM 7
Monday 2 September
1.00pm – c2.00pm

Purcell
Sound the Trumpet   3'

Purcell, arr. Britten
Sequence of pieces including
Morning Hymn   3'
In the Black Dismal Dungeon
of Despair   5'
The Queen's Epicedium   8'
Evening Hymn   5'

Judith Weir
Ox Mountain Covered
by Trees   5'

Britten
Canticle No. 2: Abraham
and Isaac   17'

Michael Chance counter-tenor
Mark Padmore tenor
Roger Vignoles piano

Three masterly composers of
lyric song share the honours
in this recital for the thrilling
and haunting combination of
tenor and counter-tenor. In
their distinctive ways each
composer lays bare the
foibles of humanity touched
by something of the divine –
most directly in Britten's
consummate retelling of the
story of the Old Testament
patriarch Abraham and his
son Isaac.

PCM 8
Monday 9 September
1.00pm – c2.00pm

Tippett
Dance, Clarion Air   5'

Finzi
White Flowering Days   4'

Vaughan Williams
Silence and Music   5'

Elgar
To Her Beneath Whose
Steadfast Star   6'

C. Wood
A Century's Penultimate   5'

Walton
A Litany   3'
Set Me as a Seal upon
Thine Heart   4'
Where Does the Uttered
Music Go?   7'

Britten
Choral Dances from
Gloriana   10'

BBC Singers
Stephen Layton conductor

Jubilee and the music of
Walton bring the series full
circle. Three of Walton's
exquisite miniatures – the
essence of the English choral
tradition – are framed with
pieces by his elders and
contemporaries honouring the
royal virtues of Victoria and
the two Elizabeths.

Special Offers

You can claim any of these discounts when booking by post or fax, using the Booking Form facing page 122, by phone or in person (from Monday 17 June, mentioning the relevant offer) or online (except for Proms Explorers) via our new Online Ticket Request system at www.bbc.co.uk/proms.
All offers are subject to availability.

Proms Explorers

Looking for a good recommendation?

We've put together two Explorer packages to help you take full advantage of the dizzying variety of great music on offer at Proms 2002, plus ticket discounts and other bonuses.

Save 10% and get a free programme when you book the same number of tickets for three or four concerts from either Explorer package. Book for five or more concerts and save 15%, plus you can enjoy a free selected Late Night Prom as well.

Explorer offers apply to Centre/Side Stalls and Front/Rear Circle tickets only, and are open until 5 July.

See listings pages for full programme details.

Spanish Explorer

Tapas for the ear! Picking up on one of the major themes of the season, the Spanish Explorer offers an exciting mix of orchestral and operatic masterpieces by Spain's greatest composers, South-American sensuality and Hispanic reveries by non-Spanish composers, alongside classics and discoveries from other parts of Europe.

PROM 7
Wednesday 24 July, 7.30pm
Music by Mendelssohn, Falla, Montsalvatge and Gerhard.

PROM 16
Wednesday 31 July, 7.00pm
Ravel's *Rapsodie espagnole* plus works by Szymanowski, Debussy and Lutoslawski.

PROM 18
Friday 2 August, 7.30pm
An operatic double bill: Granados's *Goyescas* and Ravel's *L'Heure espagnole*.

PROM 26
Thursday 8 August, 7.30pm
Falla's one-act opera *La vida breve* is paired with the most important work by Mexico's most significant composer, Silvestre Revueltas.

PROM 39
Sunday 18 August, 8.00pm
A Spanish-flavoured first-half – Shchedrin's balletic version of Bizet's *Carmen* and gypsy pieces by Ravel and Sarasate – precedes Prokofiev's Fifth Symphony.

PROM 41
Tuesday 20 August, 7.00pm
A programme of Latin-American pieces, including music by Gershwin, Copland, Turina and Revueltas.

PROM 64
Saturday 7 September, 7.30pm
A concert with a Latin-American flavour featuring music by Piazzolla, Moncayo, Ginastera and others.

Choral Explorer

A chance to sample a range of choral masterpieces, featuring a host of Old Testament heroes (another Proms theme), Edgar Allan Poe's tolling bells, and the UK premiere of a new *St John Passion* by the mystic Russian composer Sofia Gubaidulina.

PROM 2
Saturday 20 July, 7.30pm
Haydn's oratorio *The Creation.*

PROM 11
Saturday 27 July, 7.00pm
Dvořák's *Stabat mater*, plus Walton's music for a 1940s radio play about Columbus.

PROM 13
Sunday 28 July, 7.30pm
Schoenberg's tragic choral love story, *Gurrelieder.*

PROM 27
Friday 9 August, 7.00pm
Rakhmaninov's setting of Poe's *The Bells*, plus Spanish-flavoured pieces by Falla and Rimsky-Korsakov.

PROM 47
Sunday 25 August, 1.00pm
Sofia Gubaidulina's *St John Passion* (UK premiere)

PROM 56
Sunday 1 September, 7.00pm
Mendelssohn's musical portrait of the prophet Elijah.

PROM 66
Sunday 8 September, 7.00pm
Handel's dramatic setting of the story of Samson.

Free Late Night Proms

Explorers booking tickets for five or more concerts can claim the same number of free tickets to either of the following Late Night Proms:

PROM 6
Tuesday 23 July, 10.00pm
Israel in Egypt: John Eliot Gardiner conducts Handel's great oratorio.

PROM 20
Saturday 3 August, 10.00pm
An exciting evening of Spanish flamenco from José Mercé.

At the Royal Albert Hall

Doors open 45 minutes before each concert (earlier for restaurant access).

Latecomers will not be admitted into the auditorium until there is a suitable break in the music. There is a video monitor with digital audio relay in the foyer at Door 6.

Bags and coats may be left in the cloakrooms at Door 4 (ground level), Door 8 (circle level) and within the Arena corridor. Folding chairs and hand-luggage larger than a briefcase are not allowed in the auditorium.

Dos and Don'ts Eating, drinking and smoking are not permitted inside the auditorium, and the use of cameras, video cameras and recording equipment is strictly forbidden. Mobile phones and watch alarms should be turned off.

Children under 5 In consideration of our audience and artists, children under the age of 5 are not allowed in the auditorium. Children between the ages of 5 and 16 are positively encouraged (see Special Offers, pages 112–113).

Car Parking A limited number of parking spaces is available from 6.00pm in the Imperial College Car Park (Prince Consort or Exhibition Road entrances). These can be booked in advance (priced £7.00) by ticking the appropriate column on the Booking Form (facing page 122) or by telephoning the Box Office (open 9.00am–9.00pm daily, from 17 June) on 020 7589 8212. Please note that, if attending both early-evening and late-night concerts, only one parking fee is payable.

Dress Code There is no dress code at the Proms.

Eating and drinking at the RAH

Restaurants
The Royal Albert Hall has three restaurants catering for all tastes, from light meals to three-course dinners.

Pre-concert refreshments
All restaurants open two hours before the start of the performance.

The Elgar Restaurant offers a two- or three-course fixed-price menu with full table service. Tables in the Elgar Restaurant are bookable in advance on 020 7838 3101. Entrance is via Door 8 to Circle level.

The Prince Consort Café & Wine Bar offers light meals, including sandwiches, salad bowls and an extensive selection of wines and drinks. Entrance is via Door 2 to Grand Tier level.

The Victoria Room Brasserie offers a range of light meals, salads and desserts. Entrance is via Door 2 to Circle level.

Post-concert refreshments are available in the Prince Consort Café & Wine Bar after main-evening concerts.

Box hospitality can be pre-ordered by telephoning 020 7589 5666. Allow two working days' notice.

Bars
Bars are located on every floor and all offer a full range of alcoholic and soft drinks, hot beverages, ice cream and sandwiches.

The Champagne and North Circle Bars open two hours before the start of the performance, offering a range of sandwiches. A small amount of seating is available. Enter via Door 2 to Grand Tier level and Circle level respectively.

The following bars also open an hour before the start of the performance:

Arena Bars (located in the Arena Foyers, sub-basement level) – enter via Door 2

Door 6 Bars (located at ground level) – enter via Door 6

The Porch Bar – enter via Door 9 to Grand Tier level

The Second Tier Bar – enter via Door 4 to Second Tier level.

Please note that you are not permitted to consume your own food and drink in the Hall. In the interests of Health and Safety, glasses and bottles are not allowed in the auditorium except as part of Box hospitality ordered through the Hall's caterers.

Information for disabled concert-goers

Access at the Proms

Call the **Access Information Line** on **020 7589 3853** for advice on facilities for disabled concert-goers (including car-parking) at all Proms venues, or if you have any special requirements. Dedicated staff will be available 10.00am–5.00pm, Mon–Fri.

Wheelchair access is available at all Proms venues, but advance booking is advised.

The Royal Albert Hall has up to 14 spaces bookable in the Stalls for wheelchair-users and their companions (entrance via Door 8). End-of-aisle places are priced as Centre Stalls seats; front-row platform spaces either side of the stage are priced as Side Stalls seats; rear platform places are priced as Front Circle seats. There are now also up to six spaces in the Front Circle, priced as such. When filling in the Booking Form, tick your preferred price range (ie Centre Stalls or Front Circle) and enter the number of places required under the 'Wheelchair space' column.

For other Proms venues, spaces can be reserved by calling 020 7589 3853.

Passenger lifts at the Royal Albert Hall are located off the ground-floor corridor at Doors 2, 8 and 11.

Booking

Disabled concert-goers (and a companion) receive a 50% discount on all ticket prices (except Arena and Gallery areas) for concerts at the Royal Albert Hall and for Proms Chamber Music concerts at the V&A. To claim this discount, tick the 'Disabled' box at the end of the Booking Form, or call the Access Information Line on 020 7589 3853 if booking by phone (from Monday 17 June).

The Royal Albert Hall has an infra-red system with a number of personal receivers for use with and without hearing aids. To make use of the service, collect a free receiver from the Information Desk at Door 6.

If you have a guide dog, the best place to sit in the Royal Albert Hall is in a Loggia or Second Tier Box, where your dog may stay with you. If you are sitting elsewhere, stewards will be happy to look after your dog while you enjoy the concert. Please call the Access Information Line on 020 7589 3853 to organise in advance of your visit.

Proms Guide: non-print versions

An audio cassette version of this Guide is available in two parts, Concert Listings and Articles (£2.50 each, £5 for both). Order on 020 7765 3260.

Braille and computer disc versions of this Guide are available in two parts, Concert Listings and Articles (£2.50 each, £5 for both). Order from RNIB Customer Services: 0845 7023 153.

Radio 3 commentary

Visually impaired patrons are welcome to use the free infra-red hearing facility (see above) to listen in to the broadcast commentary on Radio 3.

Programme-reading service

Ask at the Door 6 Information Desk if you would like a steward to read your programme out to you.

Large-print programmes & texts

Large-print concert programmes can be made available on the night (at the same price as the standard programme) if ordered not less than five working days in advance. Complimentary large-print texts and opera librettos can also be made available on the night (where applicable) if ordered in advance. To order any large-print programmes or texts, please telephone 020 7765 3260. They will be left for collection at the Door 6 Information Desk.

Royal Albert Hall Development Update

Regular Prom-goers will already be aware of the building development in progress at the Royal Albert Hall. The Hall is currently three-quarters of the way through a £70 million programme (due for completion by the end of 2003) that aims to make much-needed improvements for both public and performers. What changes will you notice at this year's Proms?

Ventilation & Heating

A new heating and ventilation system means that there'll now be cool air in the Hall on hot summer evenings and warm air in the winter. The extensive engineering plant required to supply ventilation has been installed in a vast new space created under the restored South Steps that also contains a new loading-bay giving production crews direct access to the stage, as well as new dressing-rooms and workshops.

Foyer Spaces

Two new large Arena foyers have been created to provide extra public spaces, as well as two new bars to ease the crush for interval drinks. All the boxes and corridors have been refurbished, and the Grand Tier, Second Tier and Circle levels now boast new carpets with the largest single-woven design in the world.

South Foyer & Box Office

A new porch at the Hall's south end will create a grand entrance to the new South Foyer, where you will already find the Box Office, soon to be joined by a new shop and redesigned restaurant.

Inside the Auditorium

The 80 acoustic 'mushrooms' hanging from the roof made a significant improvement to the sound in the Hall when first installed in 1970. These have now been cleaned and repositioned closer together to fine-tune the acoustics. The dome above has been re-glazed and the restored decorative plaster cove around the top of the Gallery can now be seen for the first time since it was damaged and dismantled in the 1940s.

The Organ

The Royal Albert Hall's 1871 Willis organ stands as a superb example of organ-building on the grandest scale; when first built, it was popularly known as the Eighth Wonder of the World. With age, however, its power and range have inevitably declined and it desperately needs major work to restore it to its full glory. It has now been taken out of commission and the first phase of its restoration is under way. Subject to sufficient funds being raised, a full overhaul and rebuild should be completed by the end of 2003. Meanwhile, a Rodgers digital organ is being used instead.

Fundraising

The building development programme is supported by grants from the Arts Council of England and Heritage Lottery Fund. But the Hall, a registered charity operating without any funding from central or local government, still needs to raise £3.5 million (of which the organ restoration represents over £1.5m) to complete the development. To offer support, contact Sarah Dixon, Head of Development Fundraising, on 020 7589 3203 or email fund@royalalberthall.com.

Mailing-list

For only £7.50 a year subscribers receive up-to-date news of the Hall's development and special offers from the Hall and its neighbours (including nearby hotels and museums) as well as priority mailings of the Hall's event calendars and a special ticket hotline. To join, contact the Box Office on 020 7589 8212 or email mailinglist@royalalberthall.com.

www.royalalberthall.com

ABOVE
Danger! Men at work: even soloists like Stephen Hough have had to rehearse in hard hats

How to Prom

What is Promming?

The popular tradition of Promming is central to the unique and informal atmosphere of the BBC Proms.

Up to 1,400 standing places are available at each Proms concert. The traditionally low prices allow you to enjoy world-class concerts for just £4.00 each (or even less with a Season Ticket or the new Weekend Promming Pass).

There are two standing areas: the Arena, which is located directly in front of the stage, and the Gallery, running round the top of the Hall. All spaces are unreserved.

Day Prommers

Over 500 Arena and Gallery tickets (priced £4.00) go on sale to the Day Prommers 30 minutes before doors open (one hour before on days when there are Pre-Prom talks). These tickets cannot be booked in advance, so even if all seats have been sold, you always have a good chance of getting in (though early queuing is obviously advisable for the more popular concerts). You must buy your ticket in person.

Day tickets are available (for cash only) at Door 11 (Arena) and Door 10 (Gallery), not at the Box Office. If in doubt about where to go, Royal Albert Hall stewards will point you in the right direction.

Season Tickets

Dedicated Prommers can save money by purchasing Arena or Gallery Season Tickets covering either the whole Proms season or only the first or second half (ie Proms 1–36 or Proms 37–72).

Season Ticket-holders benefit from:
• guaranteed entrance (until 10 minutes before each concert)
• great savings – prices can work out at less than £2.00 per concert
• guaranteed entrance to the Last Night for Whole Season Ticket-holders and special access to a reserved allocation of Last Night tickets for Half Season Ticket-holders. See *opposite page*.

Please note that Season Ticket-holders arriving at the Royal Albert Hall later than 10 minutes before a concert are not guaranteed entry and may be asked, in certain circumstances, to join the day queue.

For further details and prices of Season Tickets, see page 121.

Weekend Promming Pass

A new Weekend Promming Pass is now available. Benefits include guaranteed access to Proms at weekends and savings against Day Promming. *For full details, see page 113*

Where to Queue

● Arena Day Queue
  Enter by Door 11

● Gallery Day Queue
  Enter by Door 10

● Arena Season Queue
  Enter by Door 2

● Gallery Season Queue
  Enter by Door 3

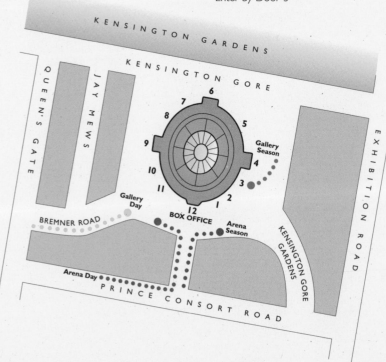

The Last Night

Owing to the huge demand for Last Night tickets, special booking arrangements apply. Your best chance of purchasing tickets for the Last Night of the Proms is through the Priority Booking system

Priority Booking for the Last Night

The Six Concert Rule

In order to apply for any tickets for the Last Night during the Priority Booking period (ie. before General Booking opens on Monday 17 June), you must book for at least six other concerts in the 2002 season.

Book one ticket in the same seating area for at least six other concerts in the 2002 season and you can apply at the same time for a single ticket in the same seating area for the Last Night. For example, book a ticket in the Choir for six concerts, and you can apply for one ticket in the Choir for the Last Night.

Book two or more tickets in the same seating area for at least six other concerts in the 2002 season and you can apply at the same time for a maximum of two tickets in the same seating area for the Last Night (ie. whether you book two or 22 Stalls tickets for six concerts, you can still apply for only two Stalls tickets for the Last Night).

Note that, if you book tickets for at least six other concerts but in different seating areas, you will be allocated Last Night seats in the area of the majority of your bookings (unless you specify that lower-priced tickets are desired).

We regret that, if the Last Night is sold out by the time your application is processed, no refunds for other tickets purchased will be payable.

General Booking for the Last Night

Once General Booking opens (on Monday 17 June), the 'Six Concert Rule' no longer applies. Note, however, that Last Night tickets have usually sold out by this stage.

Please note that, for all Last Night bookings, only one application (for a maximum of two tickets) can be made per household.

Promming at the Last Night

Day Prommers and Weekend Promming Pass holders who have attended six or more other concerts (in either the Arena or the Gallery) can buy one ticket each for the Last Night (priced £4.00) on presentation of their used tickets at the Box Office from any time after Wednesday 24 July *(subject to availability).*

Season Ticket-holders Whole Season Tickets include admission to the Last Night. A limited allocation of Last Night places is also reserved for Half Season Ticket-holders. Holders of First Half Season Tickets can buy one ticket each (priced £4.00) at the Box Office from Wednesday 24 July *(subject to availability).* Holders of Second Half Season Tickets can buy tickets in the same way from Wednesday 21 August.

Queuing Whole Season Ticket-holders and other Prommers with Last Night tickets are guaranteed entrance until 10 minutes before the concert. All Prommers (Day or Season) with Last Night tickets should queue at Door 2 (Arena) or Door 3 (Gallery).

Sleeping Out There has long been a tradition of Prommers with Last Night tickets sleeping out overnight to secure the best standing places nearest the front of the Arena. The official queue will form at 4.00pm on the last Friday of the season at Door 2 (Arena) or Door 3 (Gallery). Those also wishing to attend Prom 72 will be given numbered slips to reserve their places in the queue but must return in person immediately after the end of the concert.

On the Night A small number of standing tickets may be available on the Last Night itself (priced £4.00), one per person, just before the start of the concert. No previous ticket purchases are necessary. If you wish to take a chance, join the queue at Door 11 (Arena) or Door 10 (Gallery).

Choose your seating area

Choir
Circle (restricted view)
Side Stalls
Arena (standing)
Loggia Boxes
Centre Stalls
2nd Tier Boxes
Circle (Front/Rear)
Gallery (standing)

ORGAN

STAGE

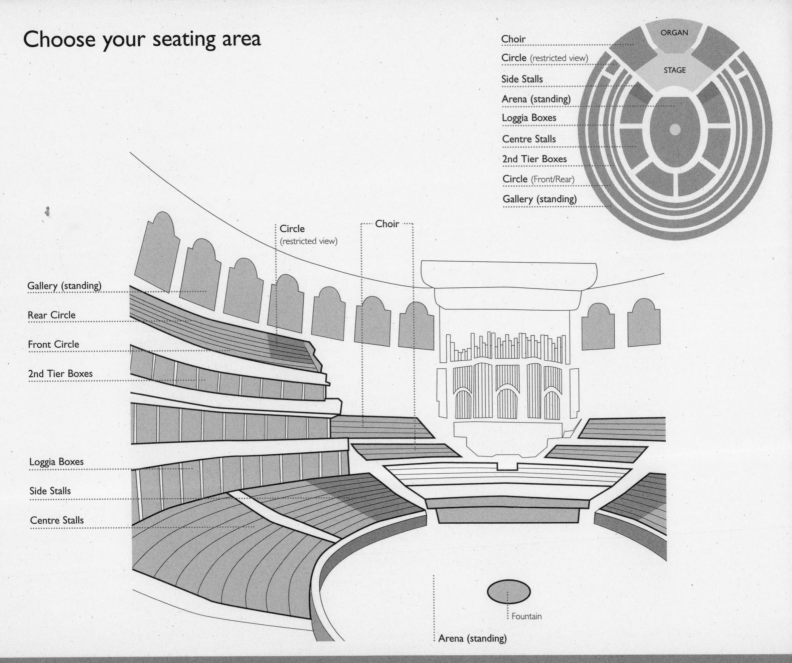

Circle
(restricted view)

Choir

Gallery (standing)

Rear Circle

Front Circle

2nd Tier Boxes

Loggia Boxes

Side Stalls

Centre Stalls

Fountain

Arena (standing)

Price Bands for Proms in the Royal Albert Hall

Seats

Each concert falls into one of seven different price bands, colour coded for easy reference

	A	B	C	D	E	F	G
Centre Stalls	£23.00	£30.00	£38.00	£12.50	£15.00	£73.00	
Side Stalls	£21.50	£27.00	£35.00	£12.50	£15.00	£70.00	
Loggia Boxes (8 seats)	£25.00	£32.50	£40.00	£12.50	£15.00	£75.00	
2nd Tier Boxes (5 seats)	£17.50	£22.50	£32.00	£12.50	£15.00	£70.00	
Choir	£15.00	£18.00	£24.00	£9.00	£12.50	£52.50	
Front Circle	£13.00	£16.00	£20.00	£9.00	£12.50	£52.50	
Rear Circle	£10.00	£11.00	£14.50	£9.00	£12.50	£40.00	
Circle (restricted view)	£6.00	£7.00	£10.00			£20.00	

ALL SEATS £10.00 (UNDER 16s £5.00)

Promming

Standing places are available in the Arena and Gallery on the day for £4.00 (see page 118)

Season Tickets	Dates	Arena	Gallery
Whole Season (Proms 1–73)	19 July – 14 September	**£160.00**	**£135.00**
Half Season tickets			
First Half (Proms 1–36)	19 July – 16 August	**£90.00**	**£75.00**
Second Half (Proms 37–72)	17 August – 13 September	**£90.00**	**£75.00**

BBC Proms in the Park, London, Saturday 14 September

All tickets £17.00 (for further details of this and other Proms in the Park venues, see page 109)

CBBC Prom in the Park, London, Sunday 15 September

Adults £11.00   **Children (3–16 yrs) £7.00**   **Under-3s free**

BBC Blue Planet Prom in the Park, London, Sunday 15 September

All tickets £15.00

Please note that booking fees apply to all postal, fax, telephone and online bookings (for details, see Booking Form)

Fold-out price guide

For a handy reminder of standard ticket prices and special offers, keep this flap folded out while browsing the listings.

How to book

Priority Booking

By post, fax and online – opens Monday 20 May

General Booking

In person, by phone or online – opens Monday 17 June

BBC Proms, Box Office, Royal Albert Hall, London SW7 2AP

Tel: 020 7589 8212
Fax: 020 7581 9311

Online: www.bbc.co.uk/proms

How to fill in the Booking Form

- **Choose the concerts** you want to go to and where you want to sit.

- **Enter the number of tickets** you require for each concert under your chosen seating area.

- **Add up the value of tickets** requested and enter the amount in the 'Sub-total' column.

- **For Proms Explorer offers** (see page 112) complete the special section of the Booking Form. Note that you must book the same number of tickets from the same package and in the same seating area for each of your chosen concerts.

- **For any other Special Offers** (see page 113), tick the 'discount claimed' column and enter the value of the discount in the 'Discount' column. Subtract the value of the discount from the sub-total and enter the 'Total' at the end of the row.

- **For Under-16 discounts** enter the number of adults within the white area, the number of under-16s within the blue area.

- **If the tickets you want are not available**, lower-priced tickets for the same concert will be sent. Please tick the box at the end of the Booking Form if this is not acceptable.

- **Tickets cannot be exchanged** for other performances nor refunded except in the event of a cancelled performance.

Booking Queries

If you have any queries about how to fill in the Booking Form, call the Box Office on 020 7589 8212 from 29 April (open 9.00am–9.00pm daily).

Fax Booking

If booking by fax, clearly state your name on all three pages. Please note that fax booking lines are open 24 hours a day. Please do not duplicate your booking by post or online.

Online Booking

For details of how to book online, visit the BBC Proms website at www.bbc.co.uk/proms

BOOKING FORM PART I

Full name of sender (Fax Booking)   Surname D'ANTINO   First Name ANNE

Seating Area: please indicate number of seats required

Prom	Date	Time	Price Code	Special Offers See pages 112-113	Centre Stalls	Side Stalls	Loggia Boxes (8 seats)	2nd Tier Boxes (5 seats)	Front Circle	Choir	Rear Circle	Circle (restricted view)	Wheelchair space See page 116	Sub-total (£)	Please tick if discount claimed	Discount (£)	Car Parking See page 115	Total (£)	Office Use
1	Friday 19 July	7.30	C							2				32:00				32:00	
2	Saturday 20 July	7.30	B	G	Number of adults				Number of under-16s										
3	Sunday 21 July	7.00	A	G 16															
4	Monday 22 July	7.30	A	G										23:00			✓	30:00	
5	Tuesday 23 July	7.00	A	G ⇄															
6	Tuesday 23 July	10.00	E	⇄	1														
7	Wednesday 24 July	7.30	A	G ⇄															
8	Thursday 25 July	7.00	A	G										69:00				69:00	
9	Thursday 25 July	10.00	E	⇄					✗					45:00	✓	6:00		39:00	
10	Friday 26 July	7.30	A	G ⇄	3														
11	Saturday 27 July	7.00	A	G ⇄	3				✗					60:00	✓	15:00		45:00	
12	Saturday 27 July	10.00	E	⇄						2 2									
13	Sunday 28 July	7.30	A	G															
14	Monday 29 July	7.30	A	G 16															
69	Tuesday 10 September	7.30	A	G															
70	Wednesday 11 September	7.30	B	G									12	132:00	✓	13:20		118:80	
71	Thursday 12 September	7.30	B	G															
72	Friday 13 September	7.30	B																
73	Saturday 14 September	7.30	F											Sub-total				333:80	

BBC Proms in the Park

This year, audiences in London, Belfast and Gateshead all get to share in the special atmosphere of the Last Night of the Proms. Plus, to round the season off, CBBC and *Blue Planet* come to Hyde Park

Last year, BBC Proms in the Park took place at more venues than ever before. Though festivities were understandably muted in the wake of 11 September, huge crowds all over the country shared in the unique communal spirit of the Last Night of the Proms. In addition to the regular event in London's Hyde Park, there were first-time get-togethers in Gateshead's glittering Baltic Square and outside the giant futuristic 'biomes' of the newly opened Eden Project in St Austell, while Liverpool joined in for a second year running.

This year, hopefully, things will be back to normal both inside and outside the Royal Albert Hall, and BBC Proms in the Park are extending their reach even further afield, crossing the water for the very first time with a live open-air event in Belfast's Donegal Square featuring the Ulster Orchestra.

In Gateshead, Baltic Square will once more be staging a Tyneside musical feast, featuring star percussionist Evelyn Glennie and the Northern Sinfonia.

And in Hyde Park, Terry Wogan will be hosting the seventh Last Night beneath the stars, with international opera singers Lesley Garrett and José Cura joining the amazing African *a cappella* choir, Ladysmith Black Mambazo.

And remember: the fun doesn't end there! Turn the page to find out more about the following day's CBBC and *Blue Planet* Proms.

For further details and booking information, see page 109

BBC Proms in the Park, London, will be broadcast live on BBC Radio 2. BBC Proms in the Park, Belfast and Gateshead will be broadcast on their nearest local BBC Radio stations. Highlights of all three Proms in the Park will be shown as part of BBC1 and BBC2's live coverage of the Last Night of the Proms

Terry Wogan (top),
Lesley Garrett (left)
Ladysmith Black Mambazo (above),
José Cura (right)

 RENAULT – Event sponsor of Proms in the Park, London, and CBBC Prom in the Park

CBBC Prom in the Park & BBC Blue Planet Prom in the Park

The Proms don't end with the Last Night any more. The morning after now regularly sees busy preparations in Hyde Park to clear the stage and lawn for yet more open-air events designed to prolong the musical feast that the critics already call 'the greatest music festival in the world'. And this year there is not just one Sunday event, but two!

BBC Blue Planet Prom in the Park, London

Immerse yourself in the astonishing underwater world of the BBC's celebrated television series *The Blue Planet*, given a unique theatrical presentation with giant video screens and a full orchestra and choir conducted by George Fenton, the composer of the best-selling score. The evening will be presented by the narrator of the series, Sir David Attenborough (*right*), and its producer, Alastair Fothergill.

Sunday 15 September
Hyde Park, London. Gates open 7.30pm

For further details and booking information, see page 109

CBBC Prom in the Park, London

Why not take the kids along to our third CBBC Prom in the Park for a fun-filled family afternoon featuring the amazing musicians of the BBC Philharmonic, conducted by their young associate maestro Rumon Gamba (*right*), winner of the 1998 BBC Young Musicians Conductors' Workshop, plus top acts from the charts and guest stars and friends from your children's favourite CBBC programmes.

Sunday 15 September
Hyde Park, London. Gates open 12.30pm; entertainment on stage from 2.00pm

For further details and booking information, see page 109

All wild things welcome

Doug Buist, Audience Development Officer, explains why
he hopes to create a right rumpus at this year's Proms

A Wild Rumpus
Friday 26 July, 6.00pm
Royal Geographical Society
(Exhibition Road entrance)

BELOW
Town and Country: a painting
by one of the Cumbrian
children who took part in
last year's school workshops

BOTTOM RIGHT
Maurice Sendak's Max

Right from the start, the Proms have had a mission to educate as well as entertain. True to Henry Wood's desire to venture beyond the familiar, they have always promoted new and rarely heard music, and new performing talent. And now, behind the scenes, a number of initiatives aimed at involving new, young audiences have been developing too.

The Young Composers Competition, run jointly with *The Guardian*, is now in its fourth year. In early June, this year's judges, who include David Sawer and Joby Talbot (both with premieres of their own in the 2002 season), will be sifting through several overflowing postbags. These will be filled not just with scores and tapes, but with ambitious ideas in a wide range of musical styles: last year's entries included everything from a piano miniature *à la* Poulenc to the amusingly titled *Spanish Underwear* for jazz combo! What marked out last year's winners was an extra element of daring in terms

of instrumentation, harmony or sheer musical energy. The three winning entries – by Anthony Cardona (16), Alissa Firsova (15) and Chris Litherland (13) – were featured by Radio 3 in the interval of one of its Proms broadcasts (and can still be heard on the Proms website); Chris's piece was repeated on Radio 4's *Pick of the Week*. This year sees a new category for older teenagers. Will we ever hear the music of these composers at the Proms? Who knows? But at least we hope the competition gives them the courage to dream. As Mark-Anthony Turnage, one of last year's judges, said, 'I wish there'd been a competition like this when I was younger!'

A further departure for the Proms has been to make direct contact with large groups of schoolchildren. Last year's *Town and Country* project saw five schools from Stockport and Cumbria working with composer Barry Russell, story-teller Taffy Thomas and the BBC Philharmonic to create a new piece marking the 50th anniversary of the Lake District National Park. The kids were actively involved in both the composition of the music and its performance, and the results were aired at last year's *Blue Peter* Prom. The benefits gained by the 120 children who took part in the project are

now being extended to every primary school class in the country via a teachers pack, titled *Music & Environment*, which harnesses Barry Russell's expertise in a 40-page book, complete with a CD-ROM offering a 72-minute Proms snapshot.

This year students from Westminster and Wanstead schools will take part in *A Wild Rumpus*, a project that marks another 50th birthday – that of composer Oliver Knussen – and takes off from his fantasy opera based on Maurice Sendak's much-loved children's book *Where the Wild Things Are* (*see pages 56–57*). The students will realise their own dramatic interpretation of the story's many levels in film, using not just music but also dance, drama, puppetry and video art. A collaboration with the London Sinfonietta, the project will be led by its creative director, composer Fraser Trainer, and will give students the chance to work alongside some of the capital's most marvellous and receptive musicians.

As well as building the Proms audiences of the future, all this work has a wider significance. It draws on the strength of the BBC Proms brand and the resources of the BBC to ensure that future generations are brought into contact with 'living' music. These are also the creators of tomorrow's music. So why not join us before the Sinfonietta's performance of *Where the Wild Things Are* (Prom 10) for the premiere screening of *A Wild Rumpus* and a glimpse into the future?

BBC Proms Lecture

Libeskind Variations
Sunday 21 July, 5.00pm
Lecture Theatre,
Victoria & Albert Museum
(Exhibition Road entrance)

*Recorded for broadcast
on BBC Radio 3 on
Sunday 4 August, 5.45pm*

*Admission to the Proms Lecture
is free, but availability is limited.
Tickets can be collected from
the Proms Information Desk
at the V&A from an hour
beforehand. Latecomers
will not be admitted.*

Jonathan Glancey of *The Guardian*
profiles this year's Proms lecturer, the
pianist-turned-architect Daniel Libeskind

The Jewish Museum, Berlin, was 10 years in the making. This compelling building, in the guise of an exploded Star of David, or a solid bolt of zinc lightning zig-zagging across its site to the south of the city centre, was also the making of Daniel Libeskind, its American architect. In an earlier incarnation, Libeskind, born in Lodz, Poland, in 1946, was a virtuoso pianist. His love of music has never deserted him, and favourite composers – notably Arnold Schoenberg – have had a major influence on his work. Last year he even designed the sets and costumes for a German staging of Wagner's *Tristan und Isolde*. Yet it is as an architect that Libeskind has shot to international fame.

The Jewish Museum is one of those magnetic designs that hundreds of thousands of people queued to visit as a building-site and then, after its completion in 1998, as an empty and silent monument. Such was the power of Libeskind's design that the building told the museum's story – the absence of Berlin's Jews – without the need for a single exhibit. At the museum's core is a numinous concrete void, a haunting space that suggests the eeriness of a city stripped of one of the core groups of people who did so much to define it and to enrich its culture over the centuries, especially in music. This void, says Libeskind, was inspired as much by the Holocaust as by the great musical void that concludes Schoenberg's unfinished opera *Moses und Aron*.

Architecture was likened by Goethe to 'frozen music', yet Libeskind's buildings, shaped in part by the abstract music of German Modernists, is never less than restlessly alive. His is an architecture that excites. And if it doesn't actually move, it certainly has the power to stir the soul.

The first Libeskind building in Britain – the Imperial War Museum North, Salford Quays – is scheduled to open this July. The next is likely to be the long-awaited 'Spiral Gallery' extension to the V&A. Working with one of Britain's most inventive engineers, the mathematician Cecil Balmond, Libeskind has designed a gallery for contemporary design based on a gloriously complex fractal geometry. The calculations which prove that this origami-like architectural original will actually stand up are mind-boggling.

Londoners and visitors to the capital were given a taste of what the V&A Spiral might be like last summer when Libeskind designed a highly abstract and extremely popular pavilion for the Serpentine Gallery. Sadly, the Spiral, assuming it gets the go-ahead, is unlikely to be completed before 2006. Like all major British architectural commissions, there is a song and dance involved – but at least, with Libeskind, the music played is bound to be special.

BBC Poetry Proms

BBC Poetry Proms
Friday 19 July
Friday 2 August
Friday 16 August
Friday 30 August
6.00pm–c6.45pm
Serpentine Gallery,
Kensington Gardens,
London W2

*Recorded for broadcast
on BBC Radio 3 in the
'Twenty Minutes' slot
during the intervals of
Tuesday evening Proms*

*Admission to Poetry Proms is
free, but availability is limited.
Latecomers will not be admitted.*

For the third year running, the Proms present a series of pre-concert poetry readings at the Serpentine Gallery

Situated in the heart of Kensington Gardens in a 1934 tea pavilion, the Serpentine Gallery was founded in 1970 and is now one of London's best-loved exhibition sites for modern and contemporary art.

Each of the four 45-minute events will feature four poets who have been commissioned to write a poem focusing on one or other of this year's Proms themes – the Old Testament or Spain.

The readings will be presented by Jo Shapcott and guest poets will include Tom Paulin, Hugo Williams, Linda France, Julie O'Callaghan, Jean 'Binta' Breeze, John Burnside, Gwyneth Lewis, Patience Agbabi, Eva Salzman, Matthew Sweeney and Sean O'Brien.

This year's official Poet-in-Residence is Ruth Padel. The award-winning author of five collections of poetry, she lived for some years in Greece, has sung in an Istanbul nightclub, taught Ancient and Modern Greek and given talks on opera and ancient myth. Ruth Padel has been described as having 'the sexiest voice in British poetry' and been praised for her 'dazzling linguistic accomplishment, life-enhancing and desolate at the same time'.

Last year's Poetry Proms took place in the Libeskind Pavilion, *Eighteen Turns*, on the Gallery lawn. This year the Gallery has commissioned a new pavilion, to be jointly designed by Toyo Ito, the architect who created the highly acclaimed Médiathèque in Tokyo's Sendai district, and Cecil Balmond.

Audience members can also visit the current exhibition, Gilbert and George's *The Dirty Words Pictures, 1977*.

The Serpentine Gallery is open daily. Admission is free. Telephone: 020 7402 6075
www.serpentinegallery.org

ABOVE
Eighteen Turns: last year's Serpentine pavilion, designed by Daniel Libeskind with Arup

BELOW
Ruth Padel, this year's Poet-in-Residence

LEFT
Daniel Libeskind (*above*) with a photomontage of his design for the new V&A 'Spiral' and (*inset*) a scene from his 2001 production of Wagner's *Tristan und Isolde* in Saarbrücken

Proms Composer Portraits

Lecture Theatre, Victoria and Albert Museum
(Exhibition Road entrance)

Recorded for broadcast on BBC Radio 3 later the same day, immediately following the main evening Prom

Admission is free, but availability is limited. Tickets can be collected from the Proms Information Desk at the V&A from an hour beforehand. Latecomers will not be admitted until a suitable break in the performance.

This year's Proms Composer Portraits feature music for chamber ensemble by three leading British composers – two of whom have BBC commissions being premiered this season – as well as by the legendary French composer-conductor Pierre Boulez. During these four early-evening events, the composers, in conversation with BBC Radio 3's Andrew McGregor, will introduce their works to be heard in the following Prom, as well as presenting a different aspect of their creative activities through smaller-scale pieces that will be performed by young musicians from leading music colleges and conservatoires around the UK.

Wednesday 14 August, 5.30pm

Pierre Boulez, who conducts his *Le visage nuptial* and *Le soleil des eaux* in Prom 33 at 7.00pm

Dérive 1; Mémoriale; Improvisation 1 (from Pli selon pli)

Tuesday 23 July, 5.30pm

David Sawer, whose Piano Concerto has its world premiere in Prom 5 at 7.00pm

Between, for solo harp *London premiere*; Good Night

Monday 5 August, 6.00pm

Anthony Payne, whose *Visions and Journeys* has its world premiere in Prom 22 at 7.30pm

The Enchantress Plays; Empty Landscape – Heart's Ease

Wednesday 11 September, 5.30pm

Julian Anderson, whose *Imagin'd Corners* has its London premiere in Prom 70 at 7.30pm

Seadrift; Poetry Nearing Silence

Pre-Prom Talks

RAH • **Royal Albert Hall**
(Auditorium: Door 6)
RCM • **Royal College of Music**

Admission is free to ticket-holders for the following Prom.

Saturday 20 July, 6.00pm RAH
Nicholas Kenyon & David Wyn Jones on Haydn's *The Creation*

Wednesday 24 July, 6.00pm RAH
Michael Oliver on the music of Spain

Saturday 27 July, 5.30pm RCM
Richard Hickox talks to Stephanie Hughes about Dvořák's *Stabat mater*

Sunday 28 July, 6.00pm RAH
John Deathridge on Schoenberg's *Gurrelieder*

Tuesday 30 July, 6.00pm RAH
Per Nørgård talks with Stephen Johnson

Thursday 1 August, 6.00pm RAH
Mark-Anthony Turnage talks with Barrie Gavin

Sunday 4 August, 5.00pm RAH
Nicholas Anderson on Bach's *St Matthew Passion*

Wednesday 7 August, 6.00pm RAH
Humphrey Burton on Walton

Thursday 8 August, 6.00pm RAH
Piers Burton-Page on Falla's *La vida breve*

Sunday 11 August, 6.00pm RCM
Donald Mitchell on Mahler's Eighth

Monday 12 August, 5.30pm RAH
John Warrack on Weber's *Euryanthe*

Tuesday 13 August, 6.00pm RAH
Robert King talks with Edward Blakeman

Saturday 17 August, 6.00pm RCM
Sheridan Morley on Rodgers's *Oklahoma!*

Monday 19 August, 6.00pm RAH
Members of the Australian Chamber Orchestra talk with Christopher Cook

Saturday 24 August, 6.00pm RCM
Piers Burton-Page on Musorgsky's *Boris Godunov*

Sunday 25 August, 11.30am RAH
Gerard McBurney on Sofia Gubaidulina

Tuesday 27 August, 5.30pm RCM
Members of the Royal Concertgebouw Orchestra talk with Sue Knussen

Sunday 1 September, 5.30pm RAH
Mark Lowther on Mendelssohn's *Elijah*

Monday 2 September, 5.30pm RCM
Calum MacDonald on Charles Ives

Friday 6 September, 6.00pm RAH
Marc-André Dalbavie

Saturday 7 September, 5.45pm RAH
Audience Forum

Sunday 8 September, 5.30pm RAH
Donald Burrows on Handel's *Samson*

Funny thing sound.

As the human voice, as music, and in film, it's one of the great joys of being alive.

But the more you enjoy sound, the more demanding you become of how it's reproduced. Anything that distracts you from the purity of the original spoils the pleasure - and with modern recording technologies, the quality you expect gets higher all the time.

So it is with the legendary Reference Series, using advanced digital technologies to analyse the way sound behaves, we have created a new generation that pushes the boundaries of sonic performance further still.

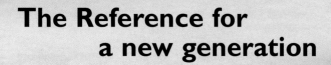

The Reference for
a new generation

KEF
UNI-Q®
TECHNOLOGY

KEF REFERENCE

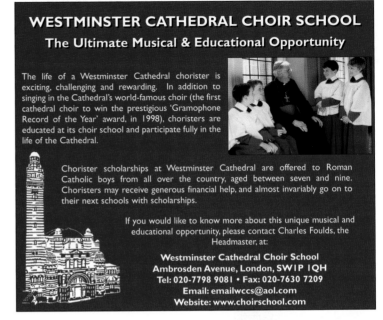

1927–2002

The Proms go global

Hugo Martin, editor of *Digitalnews*, charts 75 years of BBC Proms broadcasts – from the earliest radio relays to the latest digital tech

Exactly 75 years ago, in 1927, the future of Henry Wood's Promenade Concerts, then under the management of the music publishers Chappell & Co, hung in the balance. With closure only weeks away, it was the young BBC (founded in 1922 and newly transformed from a company into a corporation) that stepped in and took over the running of the season.

Welcoming the BBC's rescue of the Proms in a preface to the 1927 programmes, Rosa Newmarch (the concerts' regular note-writer for some 20 years) observed with remarkable prescience, 'Now the Promenade Concerts not only have the chance of a fresh spell of activity, but possibly the most potent phase of their influence on English musical life is yet to come.' Even she could never have predicted how the fuzzy sound of the early crystal sets would swell into the multi-faceted stream of audio and video signals that now reaches today's radios, televisions and home computers. Yet her sentiment that 'the spirit of Broadcasting – its widespread democratic appeal – is in complete harmony with the spirit of the Proms, which were never planned for any particular class or aesthetic clique', rings just as true 75 years on.

But, of course, the BBC didn't just start running the Proms, it started broadcasting them too. 'Timber' – as Henry Wood, their founder-conductor, was often fondly known – heartily approved. 'I feel that I am at last on the threshold of realising my life-long ambition of truly democratising the message of music,' he wrote, 'and making its beneficent effect universal.'

In those early days, only the first half of each concert was relayed live from the Queen's Hall, the Proms' original home across the road from Broadcasting House and All Souls Church, Langham Place. Two decades and one World War later, most of the season was being broadcast live on the radio from the Royal Albert Hall, where the concerts had moved in 1941 after the destruction of the Queen's Hall in a German air raid. But even then the coverage was scattered across the BBC's Home, Light and Third Programmes, whereas today, of course, every Prom is broadcast live on Radio 3.

It was in 1947 that the Last Night – conducted by a quartet comprising Adrian Boult, Malcolm Sargent, Stanford Robinson and Basil Cameron – was shown for the very first time on the BBC's fledgling television service. British TV is always said to have come of age

Stephanie Hughes

Tommy Pearson

Verity Sharp

Penny Gore

in Coronation Year – 1953. A few weeks after that regal ceremony, the BBC's TV audiences were treated also to live coverage of the First Night of the Proms for the very first time. Since the 1960s, around 10 concerts have been televised each season.

This year, though, will see more Proms on BBC TV than ever before, with 14 concerts due to be broadcast on the latest addition to the BBC's ever-burgeoning broadcasting portfolio – the new digital TV channel, BBC4.

Launched on Saturday 2 March, BBC4 boasts that it is 'British television's boldest new investment in cultural programming'. But will more Proms on BBC4 mean fewer on BBC1 and BBC2? The answer, you'll be glad to hear, is 'No'. As in past years, the two terrestrial channels will, between them, be showing around one Prom a week – a total of 10 in all – which makes 24 Proms on BBC TV altogether, or about a third of the entire season.

So what's new about BBC4? Well, for one thing, it will be taking a very different approach from its two terrestrial rivals. Instead of the usual cherry-picking, BBC4 will be offering blanket live coverage of virtually the whole of the season's opening fortnight – minus the First Night (which stays in its traditional slot on BBC2), the 'Nation's Favourite' Prom (which is being shown on BBC1) and the three Late Nights.

Why? 'Because,' says Roly Keating, Controller of BBC4, 'we want to reflect the fact that this really is "The Greatest Music Festival in the World". We don't want to pick and choose – we want to give our viewers a real feeling for the variety of music on offer.' And, in that first fortnight of Proms, it's certainly an eclectic mix, ranging from Haydn's *The Creation* to Schoenberg's *Gurrelieder*, from Bruch's ever-popular Violin Concerto No. 1 to Mark-Anthony Turnage's newest premiere.

The other big difference about BBC4, of course, is that it's digital, one of the BBC's new 'free-to-air' services – which means that you don't need to sign up to Sky, cable or ITV Digital to watch it, though you do need either an integrated digital TV set or one of the new generation of 'digital converter boxes' now (or soon about to be) available.

As well as offering higher-quality pictures and vastly improved sound, Digital TV gives broadcasters the chance to offer more channels than ever before. The BBC has already launched a 24-hour news channel, two dedicated children's services – CBBC and CBeebies – and BBC Choice. BBC4 takes up where BBC Knowledge left off.

Knowledge broadcast a whole week of last year's Proms. It was, says Keating, a valuable learning experience. 'We quickly realised that there had to be a different style for concerts on Four. We got a lot of good reactions from the Prommers themselves – they all tend to be very knowledgeable about music and

to be passionate about the Proms. So this year, as last, we'll be talking to concert-goers during the intervals, and hearing what they have to say about the night's programme.'

'We're aiming for an on-screen style that is open and accessible,' adds Peter Maniura, BBC TV's Head of Music. And because, as he points out, the new generation of TV cameras are less intrusive than their predecessors and need far less additional lighting, the unique atmosphere inside the Royal Albert Hall can now be transferred to the small screen relatively unspoilt.

For Charles Hazlewood, the young conductor who will be fronting this year's Proms fortnight on BBC4, 'excitement' is the quality that he most hopes to capture. 'For some time,' he says, 'people have felt that the existing TV coverage didn't quite convey the full excitement of the Proms. I want to get this across, to help people to understand that classical music doesn't have to be a stuffy affair.'

Hazlewood will be joined on screen by various 'mates' – writers, journalists, artists – all bringing their own perspective to bear upon the night's programme. But he will also be broadening the overall response via a roving reporter in the audience and e-mails coming in from the global audience on the internet.

For the Proms are not just a domestic phenomenon. Music-lovers around the world have long eagerly shared in the Proms experience via the

BBC World Service. Now every concert is audio-streamed live on the internet (at www.bbc.co.uk/proms), which means that anyone, anywhere, can listen in as long as they have a computer and an internet link. All the Proms being shown live on BBC4 will also be video-streamed on the website, so that internet-users without access to digital TV can also interact with the broadcasts.

For many, though, Radio 3 remains the natural broadcast home of the Proms. Every concert continues to be broadcast live on the network and Roger Wright, Radio 3's Controller, is as committed as any of his predecessors to ensuring that, as he says, 'we don't miss a single note'. He has no worries whatsoever about BBC4's arrival. 'Any chance to broaden the audience and the appeal of the Proms is to be welcomed,' he says. 'On Radio 3, our presenters – from Stephanie Hughes to Tommy Pearson, from Penny Gore to Verity Sharp – are unmatched in their knowledge and enthusiasm for the Proms. They will continue to offer listeners "the best seat in the house" – with lively and authoritative commentary and conversation with conductors, composers, performers and other key players in the season. Radio 3's online service is proving an enormous success, and this year our dedicated Proms site will offer even more than ever.'

Wright is a real fan of the new digital radio technology: 'I would always encourage listeners to listen digitally if they can, because of the wonderful sound. I can't wait for the day when there are more digital receivers available and when they are standard fittings in cars. But until then, it still sounds great on FM!'

Digital radio may not yet reach to all parts of the country, but it's not hard to find a direct link between the enthusiastic Prommer entranced by a performance in the Royal Albert Hall, the driver with his digital car radio tuned to the same event, the music fan watching the concert at home on digital TV or the internet-user glued to his PC on the other side of the world. It isn't technology – it's a shared passion for the unique blend of great music, great artists and great atmosphere that make the Proms what they are. And it's thanks to the BBC that so many people have been able to share that passion for the past 75 years.

For broadcast listings, see overleaf

For more information on how to receive the BBC's digital channels, visit www.bbc.co.uk/digital

PAGE 137

'We are now going over to the Queen's Hall': a 1930s *Radio Times* cartoon by Arthur Watts. Until its destruction in a German air raid in 1941, the original home of the Proms was at the Queen's Hall, just across the road from Broadcasting House and All Souls, Langham Place

RIGHT

Charles Hazlewood, BBC4's Proms presenter, outside the Royal Albert Hall

Proms on BBC Radio 3

Every Prom is broadcast live on BBC Radio 3 and many can be heard again on weekday afternoons at 2.00pm.

Proms Chamber Music concerts are all broadcast live and repeated the following Sunday at 1.00pm. **Proms Composer Portraits** are broadcast later the same day. **Poetry Proms** and **Performing Art** talks are broadcast in the intervals of evening Proms in the **Twenty Minutes** slot, which will also feature some Proms-related discussions, talks and profiles.

Morning on 3 (daily 6.00–9.00am), **In Tune** (weekdays 5.00–7.30pm) and **Sunday Live** (9.00am–1.00pm) will all carry updates on the season.

Listen out too for the following special Proms-related programming:

BBC RADIO 3* 90-93 FM

CD Masters (weekdays 10.00–11.30am)
15–19 July   A week featuring conductors associated with the Proms

Discovering Music (Sundays 5.00–5.45pm)
21 July   Stravinsky: The Firebird
28 July   Rakhmaninov: Symphony No. 2
4 August   Falla: El Amor brujo
11 August   Tippett: Fantasia on a Theme of Corelli
18 August   Berg: Violin Concerto
25 August   Beethoven: Piano Concerto No. 2
1 September   Hindemith: Symphonic Metamorphoses on Themes of Weber
8 September   Prokofiev: Violin Concerto No. 1

Proms Sunday Features (5.45–6.30pm)

21 July   **Deep Song**
Manuel de Falla's struggle to find an authentic Spanish voice in turbulent times.

28 July   **South-American Counterpoint**
The story of the Spanish musical invaders and the vibrant culture that fought back.

4 August   **The BBC Proms Lecture**
Libeskind Variations (see page 132)

11 August   **The Sound of the Dream**
How Richard Rodgers's musicals have struck a chord from post-war America to the present day.

18 August   **Golden Rule**
Measuring the sound-worlds of 1952 against the aural landscapes of this Golden Jubilee Year.

Times subject to change

Proms on BBC Television

BBC1: Proms 3, 12 and 28 will all be recorded for later showing; Prom 73 (Part 2) will be shown live.

BBC2: Proms 1, 30, 48, 55 and 73 (Part 1) will be shown live. Proms 37 (*Oklahoma!* only) and 65 will be recorded for later showing.

BBC4: Proms 2, 4, 5, 7, 8, 10, 11, 13, 14, 15, 16, 17 and 18 will be shown live. Prom 9 will be recorded for later showing.

Proms on BBC World Service
The BBC World Service broadcasts highlights from the Proms in **Concert Hall** every Sunday and at other times during the week. Details on www.bbc.co.uk/worldservice

Address: @ http://www.bbc.co.uk/proms

Proms Online
www.bbc.co.uk/proms
email: proms@bbc.co.uk

The BBC Proms website is the place to come for regularly updated news and information on the season. You can now book tickets online, and have *your* say on all aspects of the Proms with our popular message board. For those new to the Proms, our quick guides and 'behind the scenes' features offer useful introductions, plus there will be a range of video webcasts and interviews with this year's Proms performers once the season opens. And have fun with interactive games and competitions.

BBC4 and the Proms website join forces for two weeks of interactive broadcasts
BBC4's live nightly Proms broadcasts from 22 July to 2 August will all be simultaneously streamed on the BBC Proms website.

You can take part by e-mailing in your comments about individual performances or the Proms season in general. Host Charles Hazlewood will be happy to put your questions to his nightly celebrity guests from the world of music and the arts. Plus you'll have a chance to win prizes by taking part in our weekly competitions. For full details, check the BBC Proms website from July.

All broadcast details were correct at the time of going to press. For current schedules, consult *Radio Times* or other listings publications, or visit the Proms website www.bbc.co.uk/proms

BBC Proms Guide 2002

Published by BBC Proms Publications. Editorial Office: Room 4084, Broadcasting House, Portland Place, London W1A 1AA Distributed by BBC Worldwide, 80 Wood Lane, London W12 0TT

Editor Mark Pappenheim

Publications Manager Sarah Breeden
Editorial Manager David Threasher
Publications Officer Suzanne Esdell
Publications Assistant Hannah Rowley

Design Premm Design, London
Cover design DFGW
Cover photographs (RAH) Lou Stone
Advertising Cabbell Publishing Ltd, London

Printed by Taylor Bloxham Ltd, Leicester

© BBC 2002
ISBN 0–563–48829–8

BBC Proms 2002

Director Nicholas Kenyon, Controller, BBC Proms, Live Events and TV Classical Music
Personal Assistant Yvette Pusey
Artistic Administrator Rosemary Gent
Concerts Administrator Helen Burridge
Marketing Manager Kate Finch
Publicist Victoria Bevan
Marketing and Audience Development Officer Doug Buist
Marketing and Publicity Assistant Sara Mohr-Pietsch
Finance Manager David Stott
Finance Assistant Ben Turner
Executive Producer, BBC Radio 3 Edward Blakeman

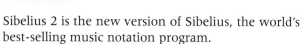

symphony hall
birmingham

'Symphony Hall never fails to surprise the ears and delight the spirits'
The Times, February 2001

'an inspiration to the orchestra...an inspiration also to its audiences'
The Times

2002

'The best concert hall in the country'
Daily Telegraph

box office 0121 780 3333
online box office www.symphonyhall.co.uk/boxoffice
www.symphonyhall.co.uk   admin tel: +44 (0)121 200 2000
fax: +44 (0)121 212 1982 email: symphonyhall@necgroup.co.uk

Index of Artists

Bold italic figures refer to Prom numbers
(PCM indicates Proms Chamber Music concerts: see pages 110–11).
* First appearance at a BBC Henry Wood Promenade Concert

Index of Works

Bold italic figures refer to Prom numbers
(PCM indicates Proms Chamber Music concerts:
see pages 110–11).
* First performance at a BBC Henry Wood
Promenade Concert